STRAWBERRY FAIR

51 TRADITIONAL SONGS

SECOND EDITION

A & C BLACK • LONDON

Contents

Second edition 2001
Reprinted in 2005
A & C Black Publishers Ltd
38 Soho Square, London W1D 3HB
© 2001, 1985 A & C Black Publishers Ltd

ISBN 10: 0 7136 5832 0
ISBN 13: 978 0 7136 5832 3

Songs chosen by Sue Williams
Recording © 2001 A & C Black Publishers Ltd
Cover artwork by Tessa Barwick
Instrument illustrations © Alison Dexter
Designed by Dorothy Moir
Piano accompaniments performed by Michael Haslam
Sound engineered by David Moses
Printed in Great Britain by St. Edmundsbury Press Ltd,
Bury St. Edmunds, Suffolk

ALSO AVAILABLE
Words and melody edition 0 7136 6042 2

(Song and CD track numbers are the same)

Notes on the music

Introductions

Where an introduction is not written out at the beginning of a song, a suggested start has been indicated with an asterisk in the music.

Play-along ideas

Guitar chords and suggestions for effective melodic and rhythmic accompaniments to the songs are included in the book. Music reading is required for some of these, but wherever possible ideas have been explained without musical notation. The percussion instruments named in the play-along ideas are suggestions only. Encourage the children to explore the effects of using other instruments.

Pronunciation and historical notes

Definitions and pronunciations are given for words that appear in dialect in the songs. Historical notes are also included for many of the songs.

Photocopying

Because it is illegal to photocopy music without permission, and because blanket photocopying licenses do not apply to this book, we take care to help you teach the songs without photocopying.

The songs in this book are short enough and repetitive enough for children to learn by heart. However for educational purposes within an educational establishment, you may, without written permission:

• write the words or music of a song by hand onto a blackboard;
• write the words or music by hand onto an overhead projector acetate;
• allow the children to write out their own individual copies.

You may write to us for permission to make photocopies of A & C Black copyright songs at A & C Black, PO Box 19, St Neots, Cambs PE19 8SF. Please check first that the copyright is ours. You will find the copyright holders listed on the acknowledgements page at the back of this book.

CD track numbering

The track numbering for the CD is the same as the number of the song i the book. When two versions of the same song are given, both are included within the same track on the CD. If the second version of a son is desired, simply fast forward through the first version on the track to find the start of the second.

CD piano accompaniments

The CD contains piano accompaniments to all the songs in the book, including those written out as melody only. The introductions are those indicated in the book.

Practice tracks

Certain songs in the book are better performed without the piano - eithe unaccompanied or accompanied by classroom percussion instruments only For these tracks, the piano accompaniment given on the CD is for one practice verse only. The following songs have only one verse on the CD:

3 *The Lincolnshire Poacher*	31 *Blow the man down*
8 *Billy Boy*	35 *Bushes and briars*
9 *Dashing away with the smoothing iron*	37 *There's a big ship sailing*
12 *The Keeper*	38 *Donkey riding*
13 *Brennan on the moor*	40 *The drummer and the co*
17 *The tailor and the mouse*	42 *Paper of pins*
21 *Scarborough Fair*	47 *Barbara Allen*
22 *The wraggle taggle gipsies*	50 *Widdicombe Fair*
25 *All things are quite silent*	51 *Johnny Todd*

Performance backing tracks

All the other tracks on the CD give the piano accompaniment for all verse of the song, so that they may be used for performance as well as practice

1 Mairi's wedding

words and melody: Hugh Roberton

Step we gaily, on we go,
Heel for heel and toe for toe,
Arm in arm and row on row,
All for Mairi's wedding.

Over hillways up and down,
Myrtle green and bracken brown,
Past the sheilings, through the town;
All for sake of Mairi.
Step we gaily, on we go …

Red her cheeks as rowans are,
Bright her eye as any star,
Fairest of them all by far,
Is our darling Mairi.
Step we gaily, on we go …

Plenty herring, plenty meal,
Plenty peat to fill her creel,
Plenty bonnie bairns as weel;
That's the toast for Mairi.
Step we gaily, on we go …

myrtle: bog myrtle - a plant common in Scotland, growing in bogs and on wet heaths. It has a pleasant smell, like eucalyptus.
sheiling: summer pasture on a hillside
creel: basket
bairn: child

Historical notes
This song originally comes from Lewis in the Western Isles, situated to the north west of the Scottish mainland. It is also known as 'The Lewis bridal song'.

2 Oh soldier, soldier

traditional Englis

1 'Oh soldier, soldier won't you marry me
   With your musket, fife and drum?'
   'Oh no, sweet maid, I cannot marry thee,
   For I have no coat to put on.'
   Then up she went to her grandfather's chest
   And got him a coat of the very, very best,
   She got him a coat of the very, very best,
   And the soldier put it on.

2 'Oh soldier, soldier won't you marry me
   With your musket, fife and drum?'
   'Oh no, sweet maid, I cannot marry thee,
   For I have no hat to put on.'
   Then up she went to her grandfather's chest
   And got him a hat of the very, very best,
   She got him a hat of the very, very best,
   And the soldier put it on.

3 'Oh soldier, soldier won't you marry me
   With your musket, fife and drum?'
   'Oh no, sweet maid, I cannot marry thee,
   For I have no gloves to put on.'
   Then up she went to her grandfather's chest
   And got him a pair of the very, very best,
   She got him a pair of the very, very best,
   And the soldier put them on.

4 'Oh soldier, soldier won't you marry me
   With your musket, fife and drum?'
   'Oh no, sweet maid, I cannot marry thee,
   For I have no boots to put on.'
   Then up she went to her grandfather's chest
   And got him a pair of the very, very best,
   She got him a pair of the very, very best,
   And the soldier put them on.

up she went to her grand-fath-er's chest And

got him a coat of the ver-y, ver-y best, She

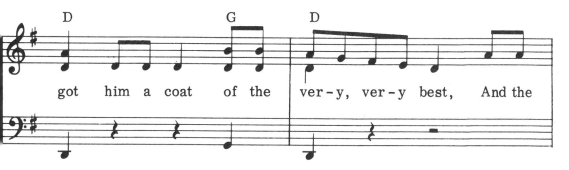

got him a coat of the ver-y, ver-y best, And the

sold -, ier put it___ on. "Oh

5 'Oh soldier, soldier, won't you marry me
   With your musket, fife and drum?'
   'Oh no, sweet maid, I cannot marry thee,
   For I have a wife of my own.'

musket: a gun, light in weight, used mainly by infantry
fife: a small flute-like instrument (like a piccolo) associated with
the military

Play-along ideas

Tambourine or snare drum (lines 1–4)
Tap the rhythm of the words:

Oh sol - dier, sol - dier won't you mar- ry me

Mixed tuned percussion (lines 5–7)
Play D:

      D   D
Then up she went to her grand-fath- er's chest

      D   D
And   got him a coat of the ve-ry, ve - ry best

      D   D
She   got him a coat of the ve-ry, ve - ry best

Tambourine or snare drum (line 8)

And the sol - dier put it on.

3 The Lincolnshire Poacher

traditional Engli

1   When I was bound apprentice in famous Lincolnshire,
     Full well I served my master for more than seven year,
     Till I took up to poaching, as you shall quickly hear;

       Oh! 'tis my delight on a shining night in the season
         of the year,
       Oh! 'tis my delight on a shining night in the season
         of the year.

2   As me and my companions were setting of a snare,
     'Twas then we spied the gamekeeper, for him we did
       not care.
     For we can wrestle and fight, my boys, and jump out
       anywhere;
       Oh! 'tis my delight on a shining night ...

3   As me and my companions were setting four or five,
     And taking of them up again, we caught a hare alive;
     We took the hare alive, my boys, and through the woods
       did steer:
       Oh! 'tis my delight on a shining night ...

4   I took him on my shoulder, and then we trudgèd home,
     We took him to a neighbour's house and sold him for
       a crown;
     We sold him for a crown, my boys, I did not tell you
       where;
       Oh! 'tis my delight on a shining night ...

5   Success to every gentleman who lives in Lincolnshire,
     Success to every poacher who wants to sell a hare,
     Bad luck to every gamekeeper who will not sell his deer;
       Oh! 'tis my delight on a shining night ...

crown: a coin worth five shillings (twenty-five pence)

Historical notes

Poaching - killing game or fishing on private land - has been a part of the countryside way of life for hundreds of years. In hard times the 'catch' was eaten by the poacher's own household. Often, however (as told in the story of this song), it was sold on to unsuspecting buyers.

Play-along ideas

Verses
Chime bars: high A, B and E
The encircled letters below the music indicate when to play each chime bar.

Bass drum (verses)
Play the short-long rhythm 'da–dum', at the end of the first and last lines:

... in famous Lincolnshire ('da-dum')

Chorus
Bass drum
Tap once on each strong beat of the words:

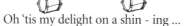

Oh 'tis my delight on a shin - ing ...

Finish with 'da-dum':

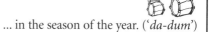

... in the season of the year. ('da-dum')

4 Strawberry Fair

traditional Englis

As I was going to Strawberry Fair,
  Rifol, rifol, tol-de-riddle-lido,
I met a maiden selling her ware,
  Fol-de-dee.
I met a maiden selling her ware
As she went on to Strawberry Fair.

Rifol, rifol, tol-de-riddle-lido,
Rifol, rifol, tol-de-riddle-dee.

Historical notes

Fairs have been a feature of the British countryside for at least a thousand years, and they are still popular today. We do not know where 'Strawberry Fair' took place, but clearly it was a summer fair - and of course at strawberry time!

Play-along ideas

Jingle stick, basket rattle or triangle
Play the rhythm of the nonsense words whenever they occur:

Ri - fol, ri - fol ...

The last two lines may be played by two instruments, one answering the other:

 Ri - fol, ri - fol, tol - de - rid - dle - li - do,

 Ri - fol, ri - fol, tol - de - rid - dle - dee.

5 Spinning wheel song

traditional English

1 Spin, wheel, spin,
   Turn, wheel, turn,
   And ev'ry leaf upon the trees
   Spin above my head.

   With myself, the spinner,
   And spinning the grey wool;
   Help me get my spinning done
   Before the weaver come.

2 Spin, wheel, spin,
   Sing, wheel, sing,
   And ev'ry slate upon the house
   Spin on my behalf.
   With myself, the spinner …

3 Spin, wheel, spin,
   Hum, wheel, hum,
   And ev'ry wave along the shore
   Spin along with me.
   With myself, the spinner …

Play-along ideas

Glockenspiel and E♭ chime bars
Play E♭ on the first strong word of each
line, eg verse 1: spin, turn, ev'ry, spin.

Untuned percussion
Ask the children to select untuned percussion
instruments to create background sound effects
of leaves on the trees, slates on the house, and
waves on the shore.

6 Cockles and mussels

traditional Irish

1 In Dublin's fair city, where girls are so pretty,
   I first set my eyes on sweet Molly Malone,
   As she wheeled her wheelbarrow through streets broad
      and narrow,
   Crying, 'Cockles and mussels, alive, alive-o.'

   Alive, alive-o, alive, alive-o,
   Crying, 'Cockles and mussels, alive, alive-o.'

2 She was a fishmonger, but sure 'twas no wonder,
   For so were her mother and father before,
   And they each wheeled their barrow through streets broad
      and narrow,
   Crying, 'Cockles and mussels, alive, alive-o.'
      Alive, alive-o, alive, alive-o …

3 She died of a fever, and no one could save her,
   And that was the end of sweet Molly Malone,
   And her ghost wheeled her barrow through streets broad
      and narrow,
   Crying, 'Cockles and mussels, alive, alive-o.'
      Alive, alive-o, alive, alive-o …

7 A-Roving

traditional (capstan shan

1 In Amsterdam there lived a maid,
   Mark well what I do say.
   In Amsterdam there lived a maid
   And she was mistress of her trade.

   I'll go no more a-roving with you fair maid.
   A-roving, a-roving, since roving's been my ruin,*
   I'll go no more a-roving with you fair maid.

2 Her cheeks were red, her eyes were brown,
   Mark well what I do say.
   Her cheeks were red, her eyes were brown,
   Her hair so black was hanging down.
      I'll go no more a-roving with you fair maid …

3 I put my arm around her waist,
   Mark well what I do say.
   I put my arm around her waist,
   Says she, 'Young man, you're in great haste!'
      I'll go no more a-roving with you fair maid …

*pronounced "roo-eye-in"
chorus lines are in bold

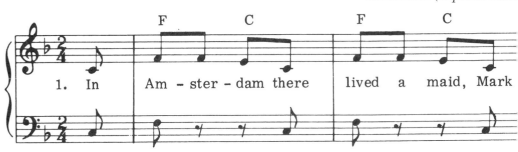

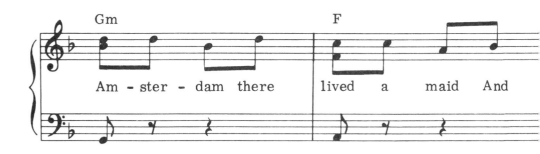

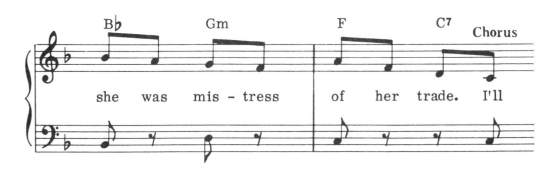

go no more a - ro - ving with you fair

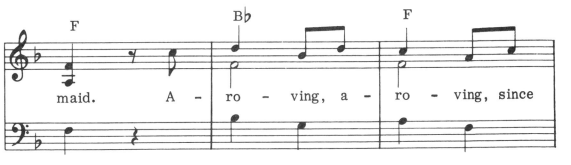

maid. A - ro - ving, a - ro - ving, since

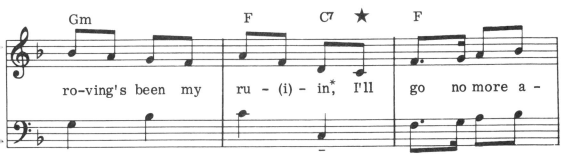

ro-ving's been my ru - (i) - in,* I'll go no more a -

- ro - ving with you fair maid.

Play-along ideas

Drums and tambours

The repeated lines of a shanty were sung by a working group of sailors. Solo lines were often improvised by a leader to amuse the men. Divide your singers into one small and one large group – leader and chorus. Play along with the chorus. On drums and tambours, tap a strong walking beat to suggest the sailors stamping their feet on the deck as together they turned the capstan:

I'll go no more a-ro - ving with you fair maid ...

8 Billy Boy

Northumbrian shan[...]

1 Where have ye been all the day,
   Billy Boy, Billy Boy?
Where have ye been all the day,
   me Billy Boy?
I've been walkin' all the day
With me charmin' Nancy Grey.

   And me Nancy kittl'd me fancy
   Oh, me charmin' Billy Boy.

2 Is she fit to be your wife,
   Billy Boy, Billy Boy?
Is she fit to be your wife,
   me Billy Boy?
She's as fit to be me wife
As the fork is to the knife.
   And me Nancy kittl'd me fancy …

3 Can she cook a bit o' steak,
   Billy Boy, Billy Boy?
Can she cook a bit o' steak,
   me Billy Boy?
She can cook a bit o' steak,
Aye, and make a girdle cake.
   And me Nancy kittl'd me fancy …

4   Can she make an Irish stew,
      Billy Boy, Billy Boy?
    Can she make an Irish stew,
      me Billy Boy?
    She can make an Irish stew,
    Aye, and 'Singin' Hinnies' too.
        And me Nancy kittl'd me fancy …

kittl'd: tickled
girdle cake: cake baked on a griddle
Singin' Hinnies: a type of large tea cake, usually abundantly covered with currants. In the north east of England 'hinny' is also used as a term of endearment.

Play-along ideas

Chime bars - D, E, A, G
The encircled letters below the music indicate when to play each chime bar. Alternatively use only the A chime bar, and tap it wherever a letter occurs.

Tambourine (verse 1), triangle (verse 2), and both (verse 3)
Play the rhythm of these words each time:

Bil - ly Boy

Drum
Tap the first beat of each bar throughout:

Where have you been all the day …

9 Dashing away with the smoothing iron

traditional Englis

1 'Twas on a Monday morning
When I beheld my darling,
She looked so neat and charming
In every high degree;
She looked so neat and nimble, O
A-washing of her linen, O

Dashing away with the smoothing iron,
Dashing away with the smoothing iron
She stole my heart away.

2 'Twas on a Tuesday morning
When I beheld my darling,
She looked so neat and charming
In every high degree;
She looked so neat and nimble, O
A-hanging out her linen, O
Dashing away with the smoothing iron …

3 'Twas on a Wednesday morning
When I beheld my darling,
She looked so neat and charming
In every high degree;
She looked so neat and nimble, O
A-starching of her linen, O
Dashing away with the smoothing iron …

nimb - le, O A - wash - ing of her

Chorus

lin - en, O Dash - ing a - way with the

smooth - ing iron, Dash - ing a - way with the

smooth - ing iron She stole my heart ___ a - way. ___

4 'Twas on a Thursday morning
   When I beheld my darling,
   She looked so neat and charming
   In every high degree;
   She looked so neat and nimble, O
   A-ironing of her linen, O
       Dashing away with the smoothing iron …

5 'Twas on a Friday morning
   When I beheld my darling,
   She looked so neat and charming
   In every high degree;
   She looked so neat and nimble, O
   A-folding of her linen, O
       Dashing away with the smoothing iron …

6 'Twas on a Saturday morning
   When I beheld my darling,
   She looked so neat and charming
   In every high degree;
   She looked so neat and nimble, O
   A-airing of her linen, O
       Dashing away with the smoothing iron …

7 'Twas on a Sunday morning
   When I beheld my darling,
   She looked so neat and charming
   In every high degree;
   She looked so neat and nimble, O
   A-wearing of her linen, O
       Dashing away with the smoothing iron …

10 Loch Lomond

traditional Scottish

1 By yon bonnie banks and by yon bonnie braes
Where the sun shines bright on Loch Lomond,
Where me and my true love were ever wont to be,
On the bonnie, bonnie banks of Loch Lomond.

Oh, you'll take the high road,
And I'll take the low road,
And I'll be in Scotland before you;
But me and my true love will never meet again,
On the bonnie, bonnie banks of Loch Lomond.

2 'Twas there that we parted in yon shady glen
On the steep, steep side of Ben Lomond,
Where in purple hue the Highland hills we view,
And the moon coming out in the gloaming.
Oh, you'll take the high road …

yon: (yonder) those over there
loch: (Gaelic) large lake
brae: slope or hillside
Ben Lomond: a mountain overlooking Loch Lomond
gloaming: twighlight

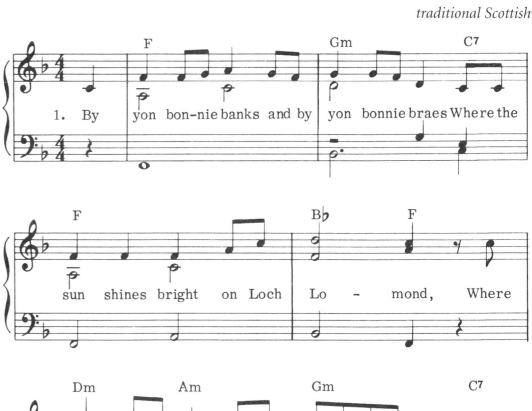

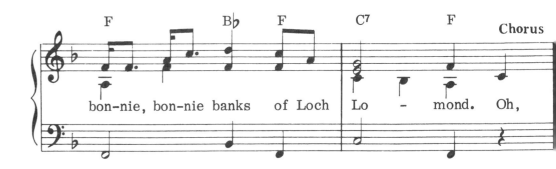

Play-along ideas

Chorus
Bass xylophone
The encircled letters below the music indicate which notes to play and when.

Glockenspiels and metallophones
Play the melody of the last two lines:

D		D	C	A		A	C	B♭	A	G	F	D
Me		and	my	true		love	will	ne -	ver	meet	a -	gain,

C	D	F	F	A	C	D		C	A	G		F
On	the	bon-	nie,	bon-	nie,	banks		of	Loch	Lo	-	mond.

11 The Miller of Dee

traditional Engl

1   There was a jolly miller once
    Lived on the river Dee;
    He worked and sang from morn till night,
    No lark so blithe as he.
    And this the burden of his song
    For ever used to be,
    'I care for nobody, no, not I,
    If nobody cares for me.

2   I live by my mill, she is to me
    Like parent, child and wife;
    I would not change my station
    For any other in life.
    No lawyer, surgeon or doctor
    E'er had a groat from me.
    I care for nobody, no, not I,
    If nobody cares for me.'

burden: chorus or refrain
groat: a silver coin, worth four old pennies (about one and a half pence)

this the bur - den | of his song For

(F) (F) | (F) (F)

ev - er used to | be, _____ "I

(G) (G) | (G) (F#)

care for no - bo-dy, | no, not I, If

(G) (A) | (Bb) (C)

no - bo-dy cares for | me." _____

(G) (A) | (Bb)

Historical notes

The river Dee for much of its length divides England and Wales. The tune of this song is much older than the words we sing today. Earlier words associated with this melody told the tale of a budge - a thief - who slipped into houses by night to steal clothes.

Play-along ideas

Tambour and scraper
Play lightly along with the singers, improvising freely around the rhythm of the words. Change to two other percussion instruments for the second verse.

Bass xylophone or other tuned percussion
The encircled letters below the music indicate which notes to play and when. The repetition in the pattern of the notes makes the part easier to memorise.

12 The Keeper

traditional Englis

1 The Keeper did a-shooting go,
   And under his cloak he carried a bow,
   All for to shoot at a merry little doe
   Among the leaves so green-o.

Group 1	Group 2
Jackie Boy!	Master!
Sing ye well!	Very well!
Hey down,	Ho down,
Derry derry down,	1 + 2 Among the leaves so green-o.
To my hey down down,	To my ho down down,
Hey down,	Ho down,
Derry derry down,	1 + 2 Among the leaves so green-o.

2 The first doe he shot at he missed,
   The second doe he trimmed he kissed,
   The third doe went where nobody wist
   Among the leaves so green-o.
       Jackie Boy!   Master! …

3 The fourth doe she did cross the plain;
   The Keeper fetched her back again.
   Where she is now she may remain
   Among the leaves so green-o.
       Jackie Boy!   Master! …

4 The fifth doe she did cross the brook;
   The Keeper fetched her back with his crook.
   Where she is now you must go look
   Among the leaves so green-o.
       Jackie Boy!   Master! …

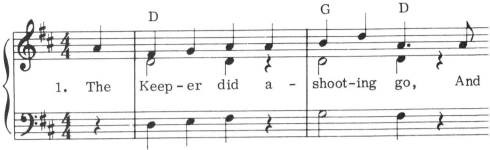

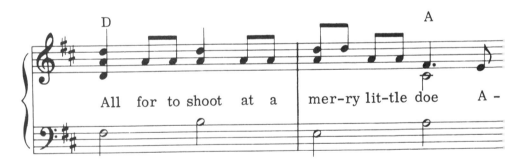

13 Brennan on the moor

traditional Iris

1 It's of a fearless highwayman a story I will tell;
His name was Billy Brennan, in Ireland he did dwell.
'Twas on the Kilworth mountains he commenced his wild
   career,
Where many a wealthy gentleman before him shook with fear.

   And it's Brennan on the moor, Brennan on the moor,
   So bold and undaunted stood Bill Brennan on the moor.

2 A brace of loaded pistols he carried night and day;
He never robbed a poor man upon the King's highway.
But what he'd taken from the rich, like Turpin and
   Black Bess,
He always would divide it with the widow in distress.
      And it's Brennan on the moor, Brennan on the moor …

3 One night he robbed a packman, his name was Pedlar Brown;
They travelled on together till day began to dawn.
The pedlar seeing his money gone, likewise his watch
   and chain,
He at once encountered Brennan and robbed them back again.
      And it's Brennan on the moor, Brennan on the moor …

4 When Brennan saw the pedlar was as good a man as he,
He took him on the highway, his companion for to be.
The pedlar threw away his pack without any more delay,
And proved a faithful comrade until his dying day.
      And it's Brennan on the moor, Brennan on the moor …

Play-along ideas

Bass xylophone or wooden chime bars - C, D, F and G
In the verse, mark the strong pulse of the music by playing together the pairs of notes indicated by encircled letters below the music.

During the chorus, play the notes indicated by the encircled letters below the music to the rhythm of the song words.

14 Blow the wind southerly

traditional Engli

Blow the wind southerly, southerly, southerly,
Blow the wind south o'er the bonny blue sea.
Blow the wind southerly, southerly, southerly,
Blow, bonny breeze, my lover to me.

1   They told me last night there were ships in the offing,
And I hurried down to the deep rolling sea;
But my eye could not see it, wherever might be it,
The bark that is bearing my lover to me.
        Blow the wind southerly, southerly, southerly ...

2   Is it not sweet to hear the breeze sighing,
As lightly it comes o'er the deep rolling sea?
But sweeter and dearer by far when 'tis bringing
The bark of my true love in safety to me.

in the offing: just visible out to sea, in the far distance
bark: boat

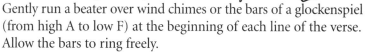

15 Charlie is my darling

words: Lady Nair.
melody: traditional Scotti

Charlie is my darling, my darling, my darling,
Charlie is my darling, the young chevalier.

1 'Twas on a Monday morning
　　Right early in the year,
　　When Charlie came to our town,
　　The young chevalier.
　　　　Oh! Charlie is my darling …

2 As he came marching up the street
　　The pipes played loud and clear,
　　And all the folks came running out
　　To meet the chevalier.
　　　　Oh! Charlie is my darling …

3 They've left their bonnie Highland hills,
　　Their wives and children dear,
　　To draw the sword for Scotland's lord,
　　The young chevalier.
　　　　Oh! Charlie is my darling …

4 Oh there were many beating hearts
　　And many a hope and fear;
　　And many were the prayers put up
　　For the young chevalier.
　　　　Oh! Charlie is my darling …

Last time only

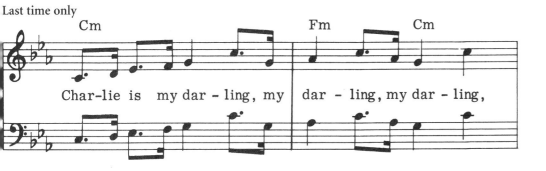

Char-lie is my dar-ling, my dar-ling, my dar-ling,

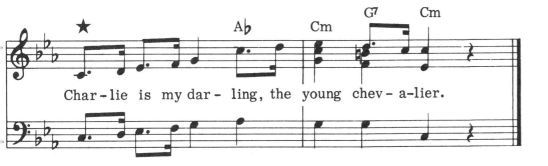

Char-lie is my dar-ling, the young chev-a-lier.

Play-along ideas

After the suppression of the Jacobite rebellion, musical instruments were banned by the authorities. People improvised accompaniments to their songs and dances using their voices, hands, and everyday utensils.

Chorus
Hand claps, upturned paper bin or tambour
Clap or tap the strong marching beat which underlies the song.

Verse
Spoons or claves
Improvise freely in the rhythmic style of the melody.

Diddling
Instead of singing the words for one of the verses, diddle them:

De da dee dum dee diddly dum ...

16 Caller herrin'

words: Lady Nair
melody: Nathaniel G

Who'll buy caller herrin'?
They're bonnie fish and halesome farin';
Buy my caller herrin',
New drawn from the Forth.

1 When you were sleeping on your pillows,
Dreamed you aught of our poor fellows,
Darkling as they faced the billows,
All to fill our woven willows?

 Buy my caller herrin',
 They're bonnie fish and halesome farin';
 Buy my caller herrin',
 New drawn from the Forth.

2 And when the creel of herrin' passes,
Ladies clad in silks and laces,
Gather in their braw pelisses,
Toss their heads and screw their faces.
 Buy my caller herrin' …

3 Now, neighbour wives, come heed my tellin',
When the bonnie fish you're sellin',
At a word be aye your dealin',
Truth will stand when a' things failin'.
 Buy my caller herrin' …

caller: fresh (short a - as in 'shall', not as in 'call')
halesome farin': strong and vigorous
creel: basket
braw: smart
Forth: the river Forth, that reaches the sea at Edinburgh

Play-along ideas

Chorus
Triangle
Play on the strong beats for the first line:

Who'll buy cal - ler her - rin'

then each time on:

Buy my cal - ler her - rin'

Add maracas for the chorus of verse one, tambourine for the chorus of verse two, and guiro for the chorus of verse three (four instruments now playing).

Verse
Jingles
Play the rhythm of the words for lines 1-3 of each verse.

17 The tailor and the mouse

traditional English

1 There was a tailor had a mouse,
    Hi diddle unkum feedle.
  They lived together in one house,
    Hi diddle unkum feedle.

      Hi diddle unkum tarum tantum
      Through the town of Ramsay,
      Hi diddle unkum over the lea,
      Hi diddle unkum feedle.

2 The tailor thought the mouse was ill,
    Hi diddle unkum feedle.
  He gave him part of a blue pill,
    Hi diddle unkum feedle.
      Hi diddle unkum tarum tantum …

3 The tailor thought his mouse would die,
    Hi diddle unkum feedle.
  He baked him in an apple pie,
    Hi diddle unkum feedle.
      Hi diddle unkum tarum tantum …

4 The pie was cut, the mouse ran out,
    Hi diddle unkum feedle.
  The tailor followed him all about,
    Hi diddle unkum feedle.
      Hi diddle unkum tarum tantum …

5 The tailor found his mouse was dead,
    Hi diddle unkum feedle.
  So he caught another in his stead,
    Hi diddle unkum feedle.
      Hi diddle unkum tarum tantum …

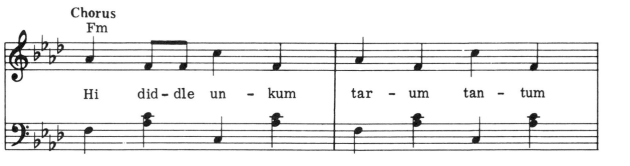

Chorus
Fm

Hi did-dle un-kum tar-um tan-tum

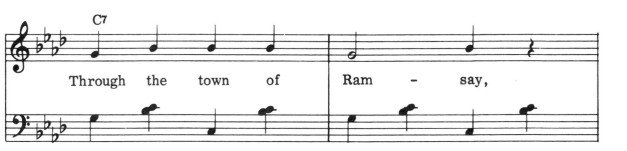

C7

Through the town of Ram-say,

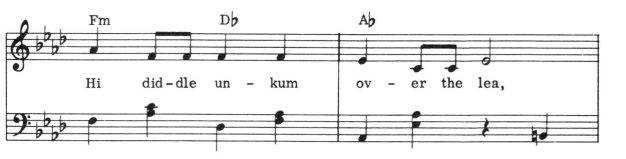

Fm   Db   Ab

Hi did-dle un-kum ov-er the lea,

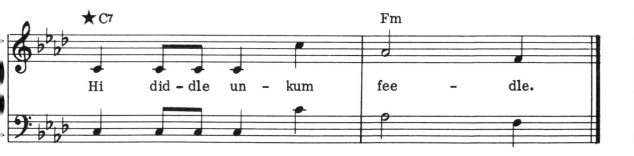

★ C7   Fm

Hi did-dle un-kum fee-dle.

Play-along ideas

Verse
Chime bars
The encircled letters below the music indicate which notes to play and when. Alternatively, if you have chime bars C E♭ F A♭ and C' (high C), play the tune of the verse:

C'	A♭	F	F	F	E♭	C	E♭
There	was	a	tail -	or	had a	mouse,	

C	C	C	C'	A♭	F
Hi	did-dle un	-	kum fee	-	dle. *Repeat*

Chorus
Two-tone woodblock (chorus to verse 1), snare drum (chorus to verses 2 and 5), bass drum (chorus to verse 3)
Play these patterns throughout the choruses indicated.

1 2 3 4 1 2 3 4

Hi did-dle un - kum ta - rum tan - tum

Thro' the town of Ram - sey,

Hi did-dle un - kum o - ver the lea,

Hi did-dle un - kum fee - dle.

18 The garden where the praties grow

traditional

1 Have you ever been in love, my boys,
   or have you felt the pain?
I'd rather be in jail myself than
   be in love again;
For the girl I loved was beautiful,
   I'd have you all to know,
And I met her in the garden where
   the praties grow.

2 Says I, 'My pretty Kathleen,
   I am tired of single life,
And if you've no objection, sure,
   I'll make you my sweet wife.'
Says she, 'I'll ask my parents
   and tomorrow I'll let you know,
If you'll meet me in the garden where
   the praties grow.'

3 Oh, the parents they consented and we're
   blessed with children three;
Two girls just like their mother
   and a boy the image of me.
And now we're going to train them up
   the way they ought to go,
For to dig out in the garden where
   the praties grow.

praties: potatoes

Play-along ideas

Verses
Tambour (vs 1) tambourine (vs 2), wood block (vs 3)
Play the rhythm of these words throughout the song:

Have   you e - ver been   in love

Bass xylophone or other tuned percussion - C, D, E, F
The encircled letters below the music indicate
when to play each note.

19 The Derby ram

traditional Engli.

1 As I was going to Derby
   All on a market day,
   I saw the largest lamb, sir,
   That ever was fed on hay.

      Singing, hey dingle Derby
      Hey dingle day,
      Hey dingle Derby
      And hey dingle day.

2 This ram was fat behind, sir,
   This ram was fat before,
   This ram was ten yards high, sir,
   Indeed he was no more.
      Singing, hey dingle Derby …

3 The wool upon his back, sir,
   Reached up to the sky,
   The eagles built their nests there,
   For I heard the young ones cry.
      Singing, hey dingle Derby …

4 This ram had four legs to walk upon,
   This ram had four legs to stand,
   And every leg he had, sir,
   Stood on an acre of land.
      Singing, hey dingle Derby …

5 The tail upon this ram, sir,
   It reached down to hell,
   And every time he waggled it
   It rang the Devil's bell.
      Singing, hey dingle Derby …

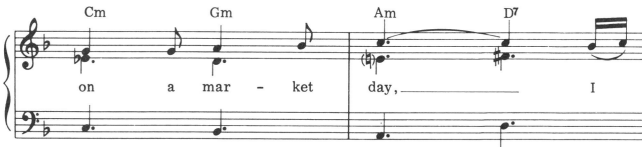

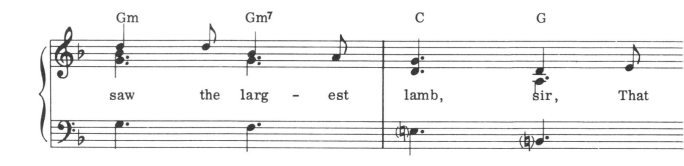

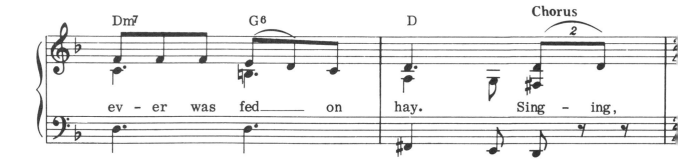

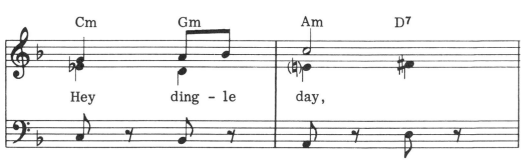

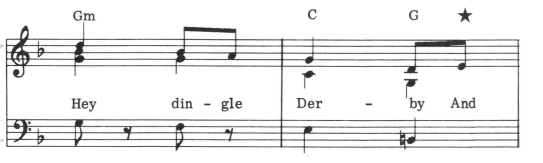

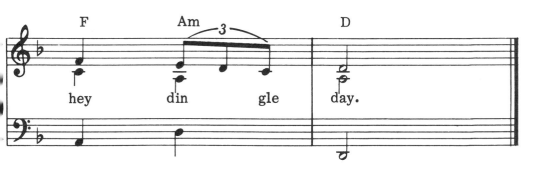

6 Now the man that fed the ram, sir,
   He fed him twice a day,
   And each time that he fed him
   He ate a rick of hay.
       Singing, hey dingle Derby …

Play-along ideas

Verse
Tambourine and cymbal (soft beaters)
Repeat this rhythm for each line of the words:

As I   was go - ing to Der -- by
All on   a   mar - ket day …

Chorus
Jingles and scraper
Repeat this rhythm for each line of the words:

Sing-ing, hey   ding - le   Der - by
         Hey   ding - le   day …

20 Skye boat song

melody: tradition
words: Sir Harold Boulto

'Speed, bonnie boat, like a bird on the wing,
Onward,' the sailors cry.
'Carry the lad that's born to be king
Over the sea to Skye.'

> Loud the winds howl, loud the waves roar,
> Thunder clouds rend the air;
> Baffled, our foes stand on the shore,
> Follow they will not dare.

'Speed, bonnie boat, like a bird on the wing,
Onward,' the sailors cry.
'Carry the lad that's born to be king
Over the sea to Skye.'

Historical notes

After the battle of Culloden in 1746, Bonnie Prince Charlie fled to the Scottish highlands, and a price of £30,000 - an enormous sum in those days - was put on his head. Charles however, aided by a loyal supporter, Flora Macdonald [who disguised the prince as her maid] escaped to the Isle of Skye, and from there to France [and safety].

Play-along ideas

Tambour (played very gently), triangle, cymbal (soft beater)
Play the rhythm of the words throughout.

Bass xylophone or metallophone
The encircled letters below the music indicate which pairs of notes to play together and when.

Middle section – congas, bass drum, cymbal
On 'howl', 'roar', 'foes', and 'shore', create vocal wind sound effects. Alternatively use congas and bass drum rolls, getting louder then quieter beginning on the words 'loud', 'loud', 'thunder', 'baffled', 'stand', and 'follow'. Cymbals may be clashed after 'air' and 'dare'.

21 Scarborough Fair

traditional English

1 'Oh where are you going?' 'To Scarborough Fair.'
   Setherwood, sale, rosemary and thyme,
   'Remember me to one who lives there,
   For once she was a true love of mine.'

2 'Go tell her to make me a cambric shirt,'
   Setherwood, sale, rosemary and thyme,
   'Without any seam or needle work,
   And then she shall be a true love of mine.'

3 'Go tell her to wash it in yonder well,'
   Setherwood, sale, rosemary and thyme,
   'Where never was water nor rain never fell,
   And then she shall be a true love of mine.'

4 'Go tell her to dry it on yonder thorn,'
   Setherwood, sale, rosemary and thyme,
   'Which never bore blossom since Adam was born,
   And then she shall be a true love of mine.'

5 'Now he has asked me questions three,'
   Setherwood, sale, rosemary and thyme,
   'I hope he will answer as many for me,
   And then he shall be a true love of mine.'

6 'Go tell him to find me an acre of land,'
   Setherwood, sale, rosemary and thyme,
   'Betwixt the sea and the sealand side,
   And then he shall be a true love of mine.'

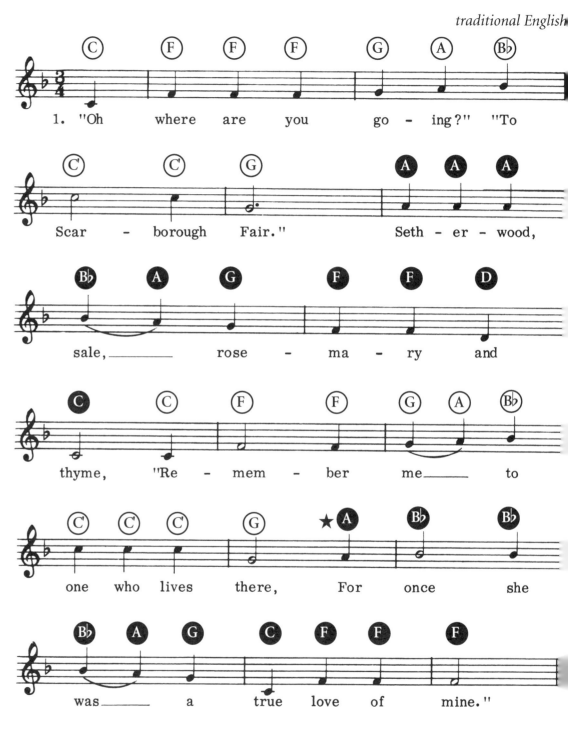

Second tune

1. "Oh where are you go-ing?" "To Scar-bor-ough

Fair." Seth-er-wood, sale, rose-ma-ry and

thyme, "Re-mem-ber me____ to one who lives

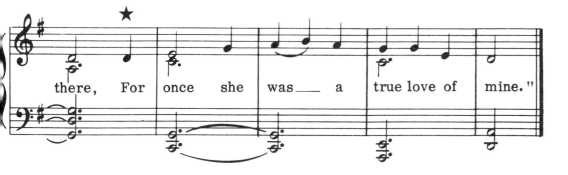

there, For once she was____ a true love of mine."

7 'Go tell him to plough it with a ram's horn,'
    Setherwood, sale, rosemary and thyme,
'And sow it all over with one pepper corn,
    And then he shall be a true love of mine.'

8 'Go tell him to reap it with a sickle of leather,'
    Setherwood, sale, rosemary and thyme,
'And bind it up with a peacock's feather,
    And then he shall be a true love of mine.'

9 'When he has done and finished his work,'
    Setherwood, sale, rosemary and thyme,
'Oh, tell him to come and he'll have his shirt,
    And then he shall be a true love of mine.'

sale: sallow, a type of willow
setherwood: a plant of the buttercup family
cambric: a type of fine, white linen

Play-along ideas

First tune
Glockenspiel or chime bars - notes C, D, F, G, A, B♭, C' (high C)
One group plays the melody for the first and third line of each verse (shown by white encircled letters above the music).
Another group plays the melody for the second and fourth lines of each verse (shown by black encircled letters above the music).

Second tune
Bass xylophone
Play lowest G throughout.

22 The wraggle taggle gipsies

traditional English

1 Three gipsies stood at the castle gate,
They sang so high, they sang so low,
The lady sat in her chamber late,
Her heart it melted away as snow.

2 They sang so sweet they sang so shrill,
That fast her tears began to flow,
And she laid down her silken gown,
Her golden rings and all her show.

3 She pluckèd off her high-heeled shoes,
A-made of Spanish leather, O.
She would in the street, with her bare, bare feet,
All out in the wind and weather, O.

4 It was late last night when my lord came home,
Inquiring for his a-lady, O.
The servants said on ev'ry hand,
'She's gone with the wraggle taggle gipsies, O.'

5 'O saddle me my milk-white steed,
And go and fetch me my pony, O.
That I may ride and seek my bride,
Who is gone with the wraggle taggle gipsies, O.'

6 O he rode high, and he rode low,
He rode through wood and copses too,
Until he came to an open field,
And there he espied his a-lady, O.

'What makes you leave your house and land?
What makes you leave your money, O?
What makes you leave your new-wedded lord,
To follow the wraggle taggle gipsies, O?'

'What care I for my house and land?
What care I for my money, O?
What care I for my new-wedded lord?
I'm off with the wraggle taggle gipsies, O.'

'Last night you slept on a goose-feather bed,
With the sheet turned down so bravely, O.
Tonight you'll sleep in a cold open field,
Along with the wraggle taggle gipsies, O.'

10 'What care I for a goose-feather bed,
With the sheet turned down so bravely, O?
Tonight I'll sleep in a cold open field,
Along with the wraggle taggle gipsies, O.'

Historical notes

The first gipsies were nomadic travellers, and probably originated in north west India. By the 7th century they had reached North Africa, from where they crossed into Europe. Traditionally they made their living by dealing in horses, simple trading, and fortune telling, which they claimed they had learnt in biblical times. The English word 'gipsy' is derived from 'Egypt', where they once lived.

Play-along ideas

Xylophone or C, F and G chime bars
The encircled letters below the music indicate which notes to play and when.

Untuned percussion - bass drum, tambour, bongos and wood block
Play each instrument in the verses indicated and in the rhythm shown below:

	1	2	3	4	1	2	3	4
Three	gip -	sies	stood	at the	cas -	tle	gate,	They
	sang	so	high,	they	sang	so	low,	The
	la -	dy	sat	in her	cham -	ber	late,	Her
	heart	it	mel -	ted a -	way	as	snow.	

Verses 1, 2, 9, 10 (bass drum)

Verses 2, 9 (tambour)

Verses 3, 4, 7, 8 (bongos)

Verses 4, 7 (woodblock)
rag - gle tag - gle gyp - sies   rag - gle tag - gle gyp - sies

Verses 5 and 6 (all play)
● ● ●   ● ● ●
What care I?   What care I?

1 2 3 4 1 2 3 4

23 William Taylor

traditional English

1 William Taylor was a brisk young sailor;
   He who courted a lady fair.
   Bells were ringing, sailors singing
   As to church they did repair.

2 Thirty couple at the wedding;
   All were dressed in rich array.
   'Stead of William being married
   He was pressed and sent away.

3 She dressed up in man's apparel,
   Man's apparel she put on;
   And she followed her true lover;
   For to find him she is gone.

4 Then the Captain stepped up to her
   Asking her, 'What's brought you here?'
   'I am come to seek my true love,
   Who I lately loved so dear.'

5 'If you've come to see your true love
   Tell me what his name may be.'
   'Oh, his name is William Taylor,
   From the Irish ranks came he.'

6 'You rise early tomorrow morning,
   You rise at the break of day;
   Then you'll see your true love William
   Walking with a lady gay.'

7 She rose early the very next morning,
   She rose up at break of day;
   There she saw her true love William
   Walking with a lady gay.

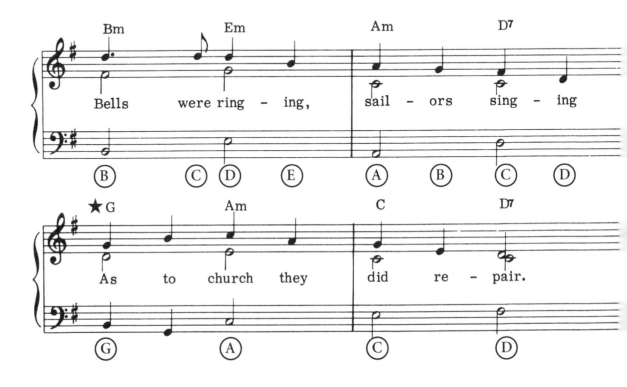

Sword and pistol she then ordered
To be brought at her command;
And she shot her true love William,
With the bride on his right arm.

If young folks in Wells or London
Were served the same as she served he,
Then young girls would all be undone;
Very scarce young men would be!

essed: forced into the Royal Navy by 'press gangs' - groups
men whose job it was to recruit young men as sailors

Play-along ideas

Verses 1, 3, 5, 7, 9 lines 1–2
Tambour and tambourine
Repeat the rhythm of the following words throughout lines 1-2:

Wil   -   liam   Tay - lor   was   a

Verses 2, 4, 6, 8, 9 lines 1–2
Snare drum
Repeat the rhythm of the following words throughout lines 1-2:

la   -   dy   fair

All verses lines 3–4
Glockenspiel
The encircled letters below the music indicate which notes to play and when.

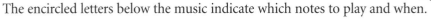

24 Early one morning

traditional Engli.

1 Early one morning, just as the sun was rising,
  I heard a maiden sing in the valley below.

    'Oh don't deceive me, oh never leave me,
    How could you use a poor maiden so?'

2 'Remember the vows that you made to your Mary,
  Remember the day that you vowed to be true.
    'Oh don't deceive me, oh never leave me …'

3 Thus sang the poor maiden, her sorrows bewailing,
  Thus sang the poor maid in the valley below.
    'Oh don't deceive me, oh never leave me …'

Play-along ideas

Verse
Indian bells
Strike together once at each of the places marked
in the music.

Chorus
Chime bars - C, F, G
The encircled letters below the music indicate
when to play each chime bar.

25 All things are quite silent

traditional English

All things are quite silent, each mortal at rest,
When me and my true love got snug in one nest.
When a bold set of ruffians they entered our cave
And forced my dear jewel to plough the salt wave.

I begged for my sailor as I begged for my life.
But they'd not listen to me, although a fond wife,
Saying 'The king must have sailors, to sea he must go.'
And they've left me lamenting in sorrow and woe.

Through green fields and meadows we ofttimes did walk,
And with sweet conversations of love we did talk,
While the birds in the woodland so sweetly did sing,
And the young thrushes' voices made the valleys to ring.

Though my love has left me I'll not be cast down.
Who knows but some day my love might return?
And will make me amends for my sorrow and strife,
And me and my true love will be happy for life.

A song sung by a deserted wife whose husband has been 'pressed' into the Navy.
For more information on press gangs see 'William Taylor' (no 23).

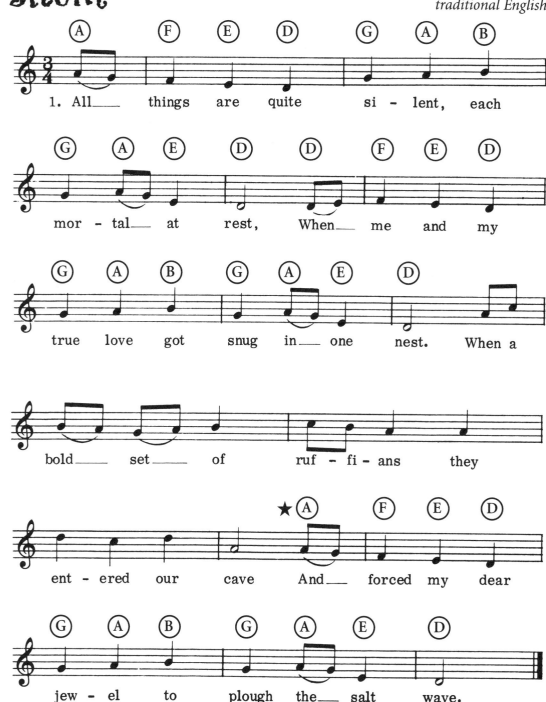

Play-along ideas

Bass xylophone or metallophone
Play the note D throughout the song on the two strong beats in each
line of words:

D   D
All things are quite silent, each mor - tal at rest ...

Any tuned percussion
Play the tune of lines 1, 2 and 4 in each verse – the encircled letters
above the music indicate which notes to play and when.

Tambour
Firmly tap the rhythm of the words throughout verses 2 and 4.

26 The oak and the ash

traditional Englis‹

1　A north-country maid up to London had strayed,
　　Although with her nature it did not agree.
　　She wept and she sighed, and she bitterly cried,
　　'I wish once again in the north I could be.

　　　　O, the oak, and the ash, and the bonny ivy tree,
　　　　They flourish at home in my own country.

2　A maiden I am, and a maiden I'll remain,
　　Until my own country again I do see,
　　For here in this place I shall ne'er see the face
　　Of him that's allotted my love for to be.
　　　　O, the oak, and the ash, and the bonny ivy tree …

3　No doubt, did I please, I could marry with ease;
　　Where maidens are fair many lovers will come.
　　But he whom I wed must be north-country bred,
　　And carry me back to my north-country home.
　　　　O, the oak, and the ash, and the bonny ivy tree …'

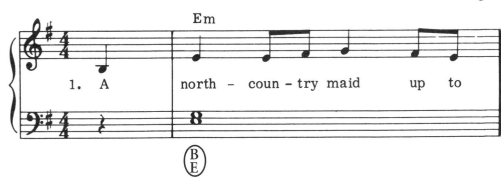

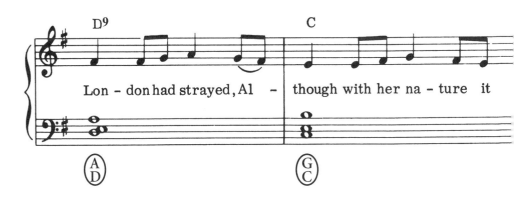

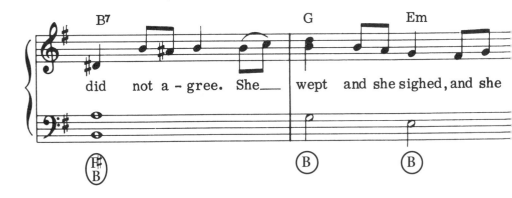

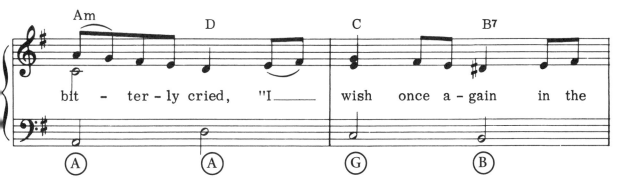

bit - ter - ly cried, "I____ wish once a - gain in the

Ⓐ　　Ⓐ　　Ⓖ　　Ⓑ

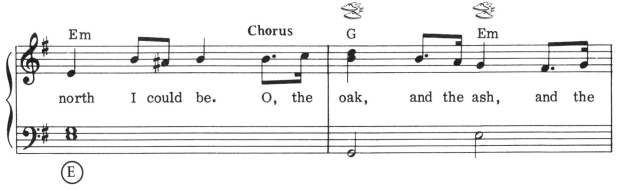

north I could be. O, the oak, and the ash, and the

Ⓔ

Chorus

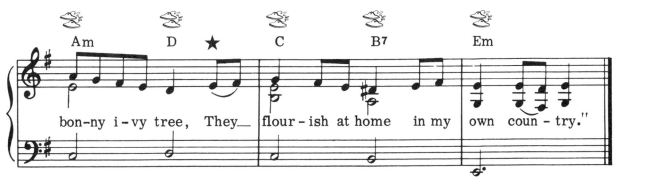

bon - ny i - vy tree, They____ flour - ish at home in my own coun - try."

Play-along ideas

Verses
Chime bars - A, B, C, D, E, F♯, G
The encircled letters below the music indicate when to play each chime bar.

Chorus
Indian bells and triangle
Play where indicated above the music.

27 The Blue Bell of Scotland

traditional Scottish

1 Oh where, and oh where is your Highland laddie gone?
  Oh where, and oh where is your Highland laddie gone?
  He's gone to fight the foe for King George upon the
      throne,
  And it's oh, in my heart, I wish him safe at home.

2 Oh where, and oh where does your Highland laddie dwell?
  Oh where, and oh where does your Highland laddie dwell?
  He dwells in merry Scotland at the sign of the Blue Bell,
  And it's oh, in my heart, I love my laddie well.

3 Suppose, and suppose that your Highland lad should die?
  Suppose, and suppose that your Highland lad should die?
  The bagpipes should play o'er him and I'll lay me down
      and cry,
  But it's oh, in my heart, I wish he may not die.

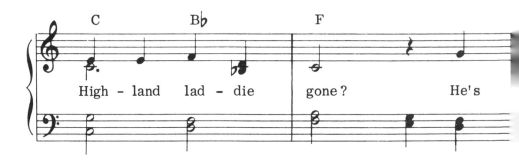

Historical notes

The loving female mourning her lost love who has gone to war forms a backdrop to many folk songs. Here, King George is probably George 1 (1714-27) or George II (1727-1760).

The bagpipes mentioned in the song are today still the traditional instrument of Scotland, and feature prominently at many musical and state occasions.

gone to fight the foe for King   George up - on the throne, And it's   oh, in my heart, I⸺   wish him safe at home.

28 Air fa-la-la-lo

words and melody: Hugh Roberton

Air fa-la-la-lo ho-ro, air fa-la-la-lay,
Air fa-la-la-lo ho-ro, air fa-la-la-lay,
Air fa-la-la-lo ho-ro, air fa-la-la-lay,
Fa-lee fa-lo ho-ro, air fa-la-la-lay.

1 There's lilt in the song I sing, there's laughter
      and love,
   There's tang of the sea and blue from heaven above.
   Of reason there's none, and why should there be for bye,
   As long as there's fire in the blood and a light in
      the eye?
         Air fa-la-la-lo ho-ro, air fa-la-la-lay …

2 The heather's ablaze with bloom, the myrtle is sweet.
   There's song in the air; the road's a song at our feet.
   So step it along as light as the bird on the wing,
   And, stepping along, let's join our voices and sing
         Air fa-la-la-lo ho-ro, air fa-la-la-lay …

3 And whether the blood be highland or lowland or no,
   And whether the skin be black or white as the snow,
   Of kith and of kin we're one, be it right be it wrong,
   As long as our voices join the chorus of song.
         Air fa-la-la-lo ho-ro, air fa-la-la-lay …

for bye: besides
myrtle: bog myrtle; a plant common in Scotland, growing in bogs and
on wet heaths. It has a pleasant smell, like eucalyptus.

*The verse and chorus have the same tune.

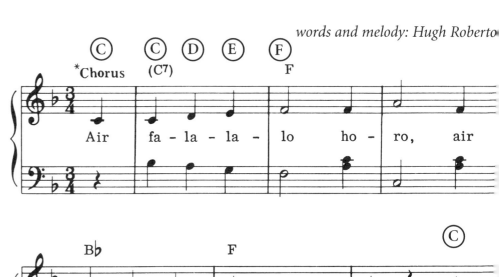

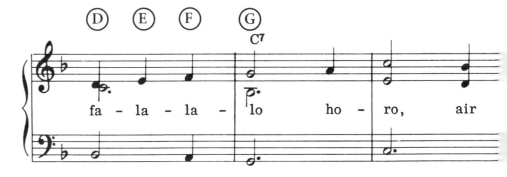

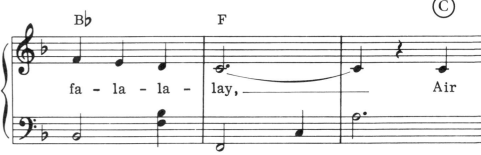

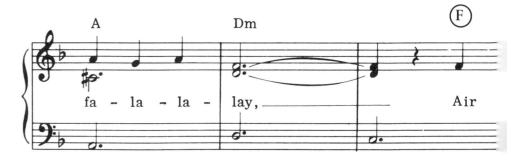

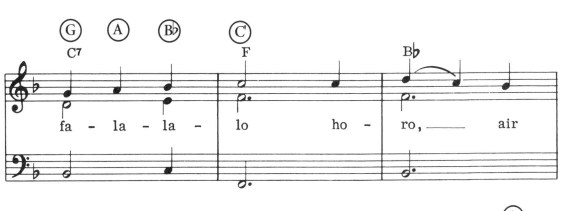

fa - la - la - lo ho - ro, _____ air

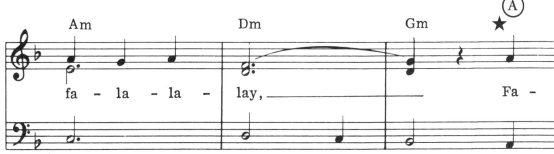

fa - la - la - lay, _____ Fa -

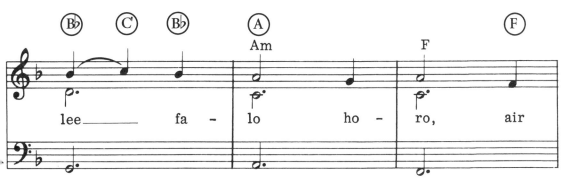

lee _____ fa - lo ho - ro, air

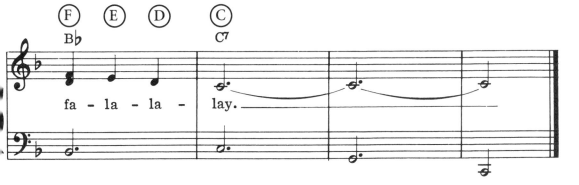

fa - la - la - lay. _____

29 The mermaid

traditional English

1 One Friday morn when we set sail,
  And our ship not far from land,
  We there did espy a pretty, pretty maid,
  With a comb and a glass in her hand, her hand,
    her hand,
  With a comb and a glass in her hand.

    While the raging seas did roar,
    And the stormy winds did blow,
    And we jolly sailor boys were up,
      were up aloft,
    And the landlubbers lying down below,
      below, below,
    And the landlubbers lying down below.

2 And then up spoke the captain of our ship,
  Who at once our peril did see.
  'I have married a wife in fair London town,
  And tonight she a widow will be, will be,
    will be,
  And tonight she a widow will be.'
      While the raging seas did roar …

3 And then up spoke the little cabin boy,
  And a fair-haired boy was he.
  'I've a father and mother in fair Portsmouth town,
  And tonight they will weep for me, for me,
    for me,
  And tonight they will weep for me.'
      While the raging seas did roar …

hand. While the ra-ging seas did roar, And the

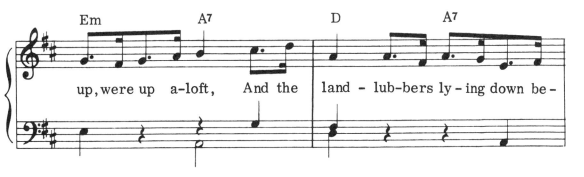

storm-y winds did blow, And we jol-ly sailor boys were

up, were up a-loft, And the land - lub-bers ly - ing down be-

-low, below, below, And the land-lubbers ly-ing down be-low.

4 Then three times round went our gallant ship,
And three times round went she,
Then three times round went our gallant,
   gallant ship,
And she sank to the bottom of the sea, the sea,
   the sea,
And she sank to the bottom of the sea.
     While the raging seas did roar …

glass: mirror
landlubber: a derisory term for a person unfamiliar with the sea and ships

Historical notes
Mermaids are traditionally associated with shipwrecks. It was considered an ominous sign for a sailor to look upon a mermaid. Such a sight foretold the imminent death of the sailor, by drowning.

Play-along ideas

Chorus
Bass drum
Roll on 'roar' and 'blow'.

Rainstick and ocean drum
Turn slowly throughout.

Verses
Play the rhythm of these words throughout each verse, choosing a different instrument for each:

ly   -   ing   down   be - low

30 Danny Boy

words: Fred E Weatherly
melody: traditional Irish (Londonderry Air)

1 Oh, Danny Boy, the pipes, the pipes are calling
   From glen to glen and down the mountain side.
   The summer's gone, and all the roses falling,
   It's you, it's you must go and I must bide.
   But come you back when summer's in the meadow,
   Or when the valley's hushed and white with snow.
   It's I'll be there in sunshine or in shadow.
   Oh, Danny Boy, oh, Danny Boy I love you so.

2 But when you come, and all the flow'rs are dying,
   If I am dead, as dead I may well be,
   You'll come and find the place where I am lying,
   And kneel and say an Ave there for me;
   And I shall hear, though soft you tread above me,
   And all my grave will warmer, sweeter be,
   For you will bend and tell me that you love me,
   And I shall sleep in peace until you come to me.

bide: stay

Historical notes

The composer of 'Londonderry Air' is unknown. The melody was discovered a hundred and fifty years ago by Jane Ross, a collector of Irish music, who herself lived in Londonderry. The music was printed in 1855, but at this time no words were known. The words we know today - 'Danny Boy' - were written in 1913 by the lyricist Fred E Weatherly (1848-1929).

Play-along ideas

Metallophone or glockenspiel - solo
Echo the ends of the musical phrases
– the black encircled letters indicate
which notes to play and when.

Metallophones or glockenspiel - group
The white encircled letters below the
music indicate which notes to play
and when.

Flute or violin
Play the melody.

31 Blow the man down

traditional (capstan shanty)

1 Oh blow the man down, bullies, blow the man down.
   To me way-ay, blow the man down.
   Oh blow the man down, bullies, blow him away.
   Oh gimme some time to blow the man down.

2 We went over the Bar on the thirteenth of May.
   To me way-ay, blow the man down.
   The Galloper jumped, and the gale came away.
   Oh gimme some time to blow the man down.

3 Oh the rags they was gone, and the chains they was
      jammed.
   To me way-ay, blow the man down.
   And the skipper sez he, 'Let the weather be hanged.'
   Oh gimme some time to blow the man down.

4 Oh it's sailors is tinkers, and tinkers is men.
   To me way-ay, blow the man down.
   And we're all of us coming to see you again.
   Oh gimme some time to blow the man down.

5 So we'll blow the man up, and we'll blow the man down.
   To me way-ay, blow the man down.
   And we'll blow him away into Liverpool town.
   Oh gimme some time to blow the man down.

blow: strike, knock
bar: a bank of sand, or silt, across the mouth of a river or harbour which
obstructs navigation

Play-along ideas

Xylophones - G, A, B, C, D, E, F, G' (high G)
The encircled letters below the music indicate which notes to play and when.

Other tuned instruments
Join the singers for parts of the melody of lines one and three:

G   **A G E**   **G**   **A G E**

Oh   blow ___ the man down, bul - lies,   blow ___ the man down.

F   **G F D**   **F**   **G F D**

Oh   blow ___ the man down, bul - lies,   blow ___ him a - way.

Cymbals
Play in each verse on these words:

way   -   ay,   blow

Tambourine and tambour
Keep a steady working beat throughout:

Oh   blow ___ the man down, bul - lies,   blow ___ the man down.

32 My bonnie lies over the ocean

traditional Englis

1   My bonnie lies over the ocean,
    My bonnie lies over the sea,
    My bonnie lies over the ocean,
    O bring back my bonnie to me.

        Bring back, bring back,
        O bring back my bonnie to me, to me.
        Bring back, bring back,
        O bring back my bonnie to me.

2   Last night as I lay on my pillow
    Last night as I lay on my bed,
    Last night as I lay on my pillow,
    I dreamed that my bonnie was dead.
        Bring back, bring back …

3   O blow ye winds over the ocean,
    O blow ye winds over the sea,
    O blow ye winds over the ocean,
    And bring back my bonnie to me.
        Bring back, bring back …

4   The winds have blown over the ocean,
    The winds have blown over the sea,
    The winds have blown over the ocean,
    And brought back my bonnie to me.
        Bring back, bring back …

33 Spanish Ladies

traditional Engl[ish]

1 Farewell and adieu unto you, Spanish Ladies,
   Farewell and adieu to you, Ladies of Spain.
   For we've received orders to sail for old England;
   But we hope in a short time to see you again.

        We'll rant and we'll rove like true British sailors.
        We'll rant and we'll rove o'er all the salt seas,
        Until we strike soundings in the Channel of
           old England.
        From Ushant to Scilly is thirty-five leagues.

2 We hove our ship to, with the wind at sou'west,
      boys,
   We hove our ship to, for to strike soundings clear.
   Then filled the main tops'l and bore right away,
      boys,
   And straight up the Channel our course we did
      steer.
        We'll rant and we'll rove …

3 The first land we made, it is known as the Deadman.
   Then Ram Head, off Plymouth, Start, Portland and
      Wight.
   We sailed then by Beachy, by Fairlee and Dungeness,
   Until we came abreast of the South Foreland light.
        We'll rant and we'll rove …

4 Then signal was made for the Grand Fleet to anchor,
   For all in the Downs that night were to meet.
   'Twas, 'Stand by your stoppers! Let go your shank
      painters!
   Haul up your clew garnets! Stick out tack and
      sheets!'
        We'll rant and we'll rove …

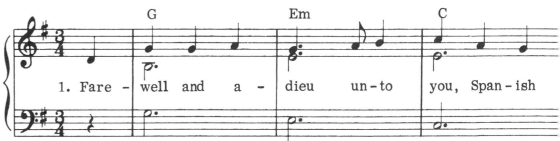

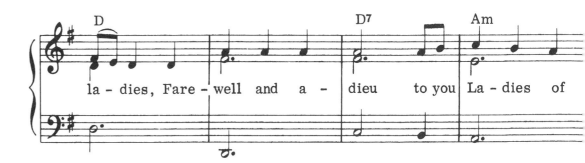

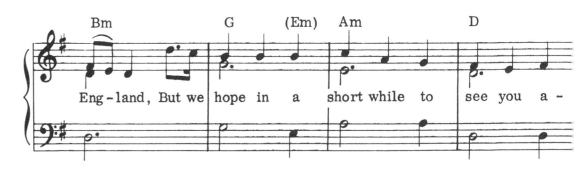

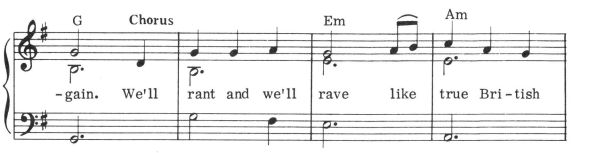

-gain. We'll | rant and we'll | rave like | true Bri-tish

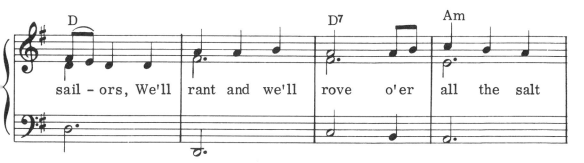

sail-ors, We'll | rant and we'll | rove o'er | all the salt

seas, un -|til we strike | sound-ings in the | Channel of old

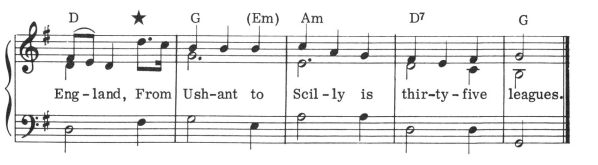

Eng-land, From | Ush-ant to | Scil-ly is | thir-ty-five | leagues.

5 Now let every man toss off a full bumper,
Let every man toss off a full bowl.
And we'll drink and be merry and drown melancholy,
Singing, 'Here's a good health to all true-hearted
souls!'
We'll rant and we'll rove …

soundings: an area of the sea where the depth can be taken with a line.
hove: wait
league: three nautical miles
stopper; shank-painter; tack; sheet; clew-garnet: various ropes
haul: to trim the sails so as to sail nearer the wind
Ushant: the Ile d'Ouessant, off Brest in France

34 Rio Grande

traditional

1 I'll sing you a song of the fish in the sea.
    Oh, Rio!
I'll sing you a song of the fish in the sea.
    And we're bound for the Rio Grande.

    Then away, love, away; 'way down Rio.
    So fare you well my pretty young girl
    For we're bound for the Rio Grande.

2 We've a ship that is strong and a jolly good crew,
    Oh, Rio!
A brass-knuckled mate and a rough skipper too.
    And we're bound for the Rio Grande.
       Then away, love, away; 'way down Rio …

3 So it's pack up your donkey and get under way.
    Oh, Rio!
The girls we are leaving can take our half pay.
    And we're bound for the Rio Grande.
       Then away, love, away; 'way down Rio …

4 Sing goodbye to Sally and goodbye to Sue,
    Oh, Rio!
And you who are listening, goodbye to you.
    And we're bound for the Rio Grande.
       Then away, love, away; 'way down Rio …

Historical notes

This song is a 'shanty' or work song, associated with the pulling up of the ship's anchor in preparation for sailing.

The word 'shanty' may come from the French word *chanter* ('to sing'); or from 'shantyman' - the manager of the men who in the West Indies were responsible for moving beach huts ('shanties') back onto safer ground at the approach of the hurricane season.

Singing was important in this task. The shantyman stood on the roof of each shanty as the building was hauled back on rollers, by teams of men.

Play-along ideas

Divide your singers into two groups – one small, one large. The larger group sings the chorus lines (in bold).

Give greater emphasis to these lines with added percussion, playing the rhythm of the words, eg

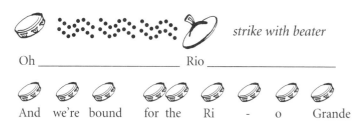

strike with beater

Oh _____ Rio _____

And   we're   bound   for the   Ri   -   o   Grande

Throughout the second chorus tap the rhythm of the words 'pret-ty young' on congas:

(Pret - ty   young pret - ty   young ...)

Then a-way,_____ love,___ a - ...

35 Bushes and briars

traditional English

1. Through bushes and through briars
   I lately took my way,
   All for to hear the small birds sing
   And the lambs to skip and play,
   All for to hear the small birds sing
   And the lambs to skip and play.

2. I overheard my own true love,
   Her voice it was so clear:
   Long time have I been waiting for
   The coming of my dear,
   Long time have I been waiting for
   The coming of my dear.

3. Sometimes I am uneasy
   And troubled in my mind,
   Sometimes I think I'll go to my love
   And tell him all my mind,
   Sometimes I think I'll go to my love
   And tell him all my mind.

4. And if I should go to my love,
   My love he will say nay,
   If I show to him my boldness
   He'll ne'er love me again,
   If I show to him my boldness
   He'll ne'er love me again.

Play-along ideas

Metallophone
Play low D and high D together throughout, as shown by the encircled letters below the first line of music.

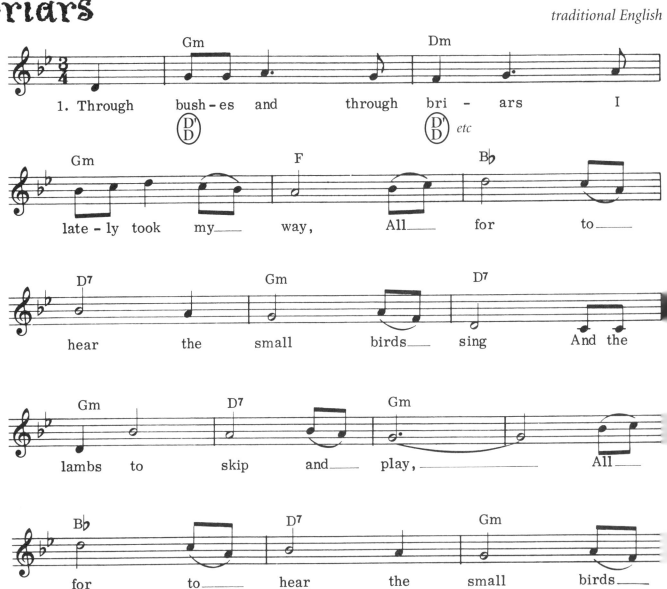

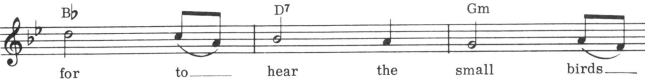

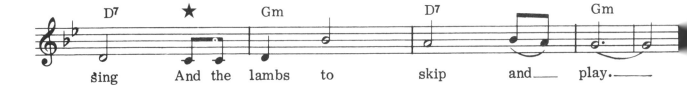

36 Windy old weather

traditional

As we were a-fishing off Haisborough light,
Shooting and hauling and trawling all night,

    It was windy old weather, stormy old weather,
    When the wind blows, we all pull together.

We sighted a herring, the king of the sea,
Says, 'Now, old skipper, you cannot catch me.'
    It was windy old weather, stormy old weather …

We sighted a mackerel with stripes on his back.
'Time now, old skipper, to shift your main tack.'
    It was windy old weather, stormy old weather …

We sighted a conger as long as a mile.
'Winds blowing easterly,' he said with a smile.
    It was windy old weather, stormy old weather …

We sighted a plaice that had spots on his side.
Says, 'Now, old skipper, these seas you won't ride.'
    It was windy old weather, stormy old weather …

I think what these fishes are saying is right.
We'll haul in our nets and we'll make for the light.
    It was windy old weather, stormy old weather …

ck: a rope used to secure the corners of the lower square-sails to the ship's
le when sailing close to the wind

ppisburgh: (pronounced Haisborough) a village on the north-east coast of
orfolk. It has two important landmarks for sailors - the tower of St Mary's
urch, and the red and white striped lighthouse.

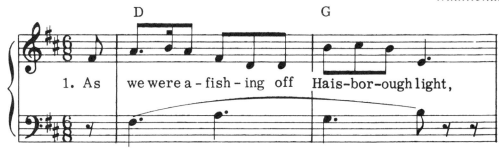

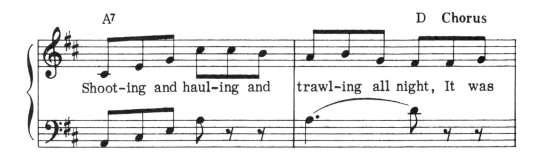

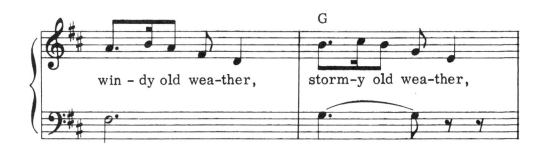

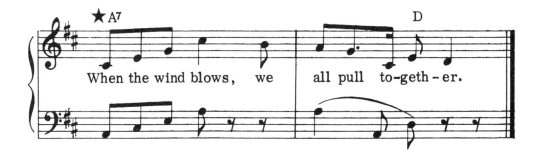

37 There's a big ship sailing

traditional

1 There's a big ship sailing on the illy-ally-o,
  The illy-ally-o, the illy-ally-o,
  There's a big ship sailing on the illy-ally-o,
  Heigh-ho, illy-ally-o.

2 There's a big ship sailing, rocking on the sea,
  Rocking on the sea, rocking on the sea,
  There's a big ship sailing, rocking on the sea,
  Heigh-ho, rocking on the sea.

3 The Captain said, 'It'll never, never do,
  Never, never do, never, never do.'
  The Captain said, 'It'll never, never do,
  Heigh-ho, never, never do.'

4 The big ship sank to the bottom of the sea,
  The bottom of the sea, the bottom of the sea,
  The big ship sank to the bottom of the sea,
  Heigh-ho, the bottom of the sea.

illy-ally-o: sea

Play-along ideas

Bass drum and tambourine
Play on lines 1 and 3 of each verse: tap three times on the drum, then play the rhythm of the words on tambourine:

There's a big   ship   sail-ing on   the il - ly-al - ly-o

Tuned percussion
The encircled letters below the music in lines 2 and 4 indicate which notes to play and when.

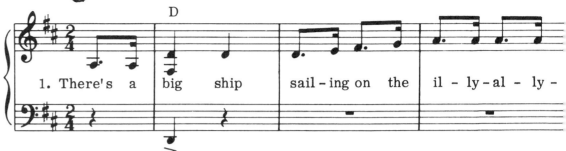

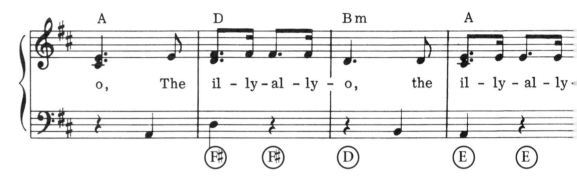

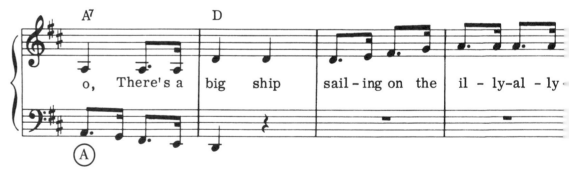

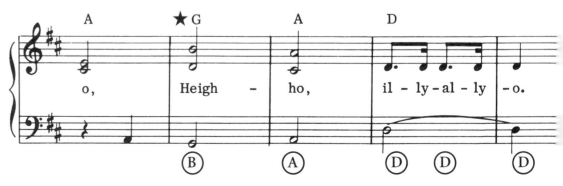

38 Donkey riding

traditional (capstan shanty)

Were you ever in London town,
Where the girls they do come down
To see the king in a golden crown
   Riding on a donkey?

   Hey, ho, away we go,
   Donkey riding, donkey riding,
   Hey, ho, away we go,
   Riding on a donkey.

Were you ever off Cape Horn,
Where it's always fine and warm,
And seen the lion and the unicorn
   Riding on a donkey?
   Hey, ho, away we go …

Were you ever in Cardiff Bay,
Where the folks all shout, 'Hurray!
Here comes John with his three years pay
   Riding on a donkey?'
   Hey, ho, away we go …

Play-along ideas

Verses
Chime bars - D and D' (high D)
The encircled letters below the music indicate when to
play each chime bar.

Chorus
Coconut shells and jinglebells
Repeat the rhythm of the word, *Lon-don* throughout.

Tuned percussion - D, E, F♯, A
The encircled letters below the music indicate which notes
to play and when.

39 Green grow the rushes, ho!

40 The drummer and the cook

traditional

1 Oh there was a little drummer
   And he loved a one-eyed cook.
   And he loved her, oh he loved her
   Though she had a cock-eyed look,

   With her one eye in the pot,
   And the other up the chimney.
   With a bow-wow-wow,
   Fal-lal the dow-a-diddy
   Bow-wow-wow.

2 When this couple went a-courtin'
   For to walk along the shore,
   Sez the drummer to the cookie,
   'You're the girl that I adore.'
   With her one eye in the pot …

3 When this couple went a-courtin'
   For to walk along the pier,
   Sez the cookie to the drummer,
   'An' I love you too, my dear.'
   With her one eye in the pot …

4 Sez the drummer to the cookie,
   'Ain't the weather fine today?'
   Sez the cookie to the drummer,
   'Is that all ye got to say?'
   With her one eye in the pot …

5 Sez the drummer to the cookie,
   'Will I buy the weddin' ring?'
   Sez the cookie, 'Now you're talkin'.
   That would be the very thing.'
   With her one eye in the pot …

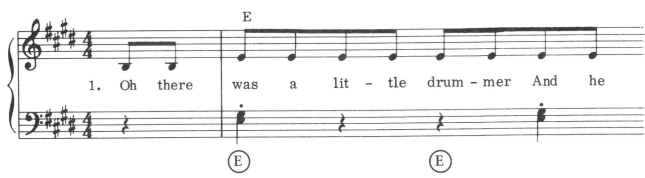

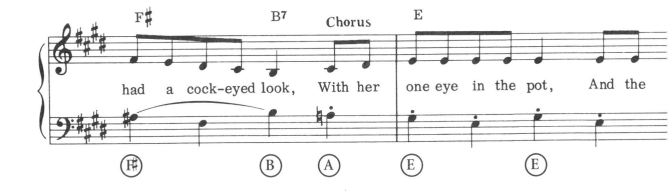

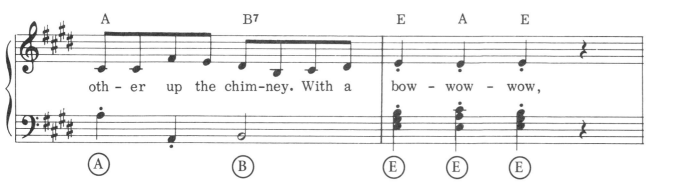

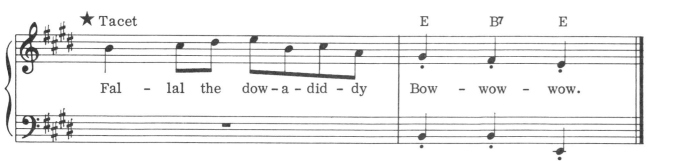

6 Sez the drummer to the cookie,
'Will ye name the weddin' day?'
Sez the cookie, 'We'll be married
In the merry month o' May.'
    With her one eye in the pot …

7 When they went to church to say
'I will,' the drummer got a nark,
For her one eye gliffed the Parson
And the other killed the clerk.
    With her one eye in the pot …

nark: a disagreeable surprise
gliffed: frightened

Play-along ideas

Chime bars and xylophone - E, F♯, A, B
The encircled letters below the music indicate when to play each chime bar.

Tambour - verse
Play the rhythm of the words 'was a lit-tle' throughout:

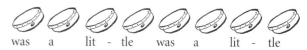

was   a   lit - tle   was   a   lit - tle

Snare drum - chorus
Play the rhythm of the words 'bow-wow-wow' throughout:

bow - wow - wow

41 Golden slumbers

1 Golden slumbers kiss your eyes,
Smiles awake you when you rise;
Sleep, pretty maiden, do not cry,
And I will sing a lullaby.
Lullaby, lullaby, lullaby.

2 Care you know not, therefore sleep
While I o'er you watch do keep;
Sleep, pretty darling, do not cry,
And I will sing a lullaby.
Lullaby, lullaby, lullaby.

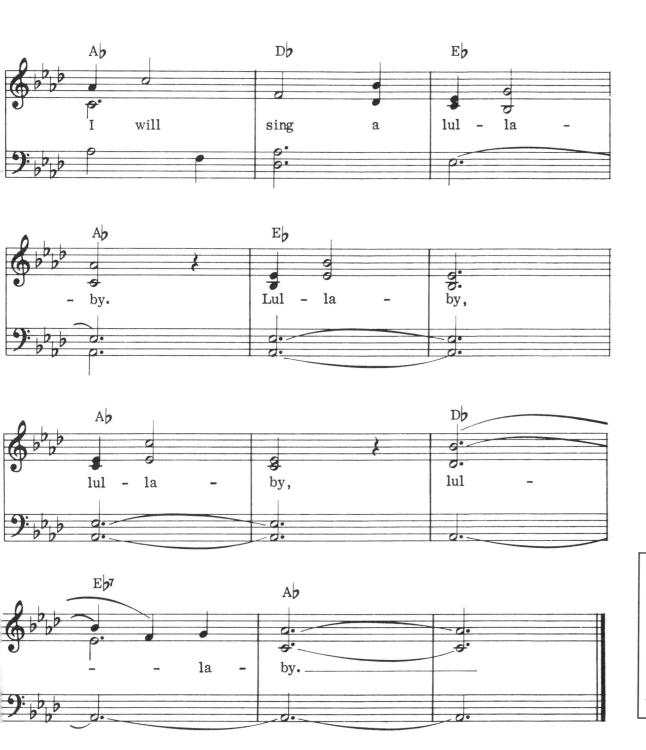

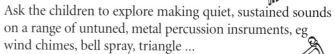

Play-along ideas

Ask the children to explore making quiet, sustained sounds on a range of untuned, metal percussion insruments, eg wind chimes, bell spray, triangle ...

Divide the children into two small groups. Ask each group in turn to use the sounds they have found to accompany a verse of the song.

42 Paper of pins

tradition

1 I'll give to you a paper of pins,
   If that's the way that love begins,
   If you will marry, marry, marry, marry,
   If you'll marry me.

2 I don't want your paper of pins,
   If that's the way that love begins,
   For I won't marry, marry, marry, marry,
   I won't marry you.

3 I'll give to you a dress of red
   Stitched all around with golden thread
   If you will marry, marry, marry, marry,
   If you'll marry me.

4 I don't want your dress of red
   Stitched all around with golden thread
   For I won't marry, marry, marry, marry,
   I won't marry you.

5 I'll give to you the key to my chest
   And all the money that I possess
   If you will marry, marry, marry, marry,
   If you'll marry me.

6 Yes, I'll accept the key to your chest
   And all the money that you possess.
   Yes, I will marry, marry, marry, marry,
   I will marry you.

7 Ah, ha, ha, money is all
   A woman's love is nothing at all.
   No, I'll not marry, marry, marry, marry,
   I'll not marry you.

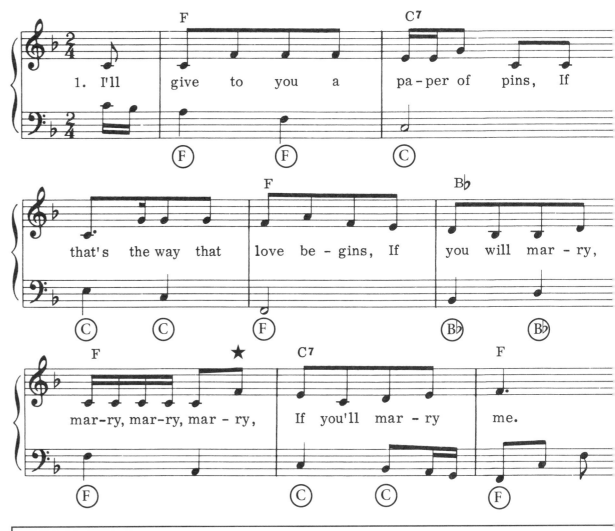

Play-along ideas

Tuned percussion
The encircled letters below the music indicate which notes to play and when.

Untuned percussion
Play the rhythm of the words for the last two lines of each verse. Use woodblock and claves in the odd-numbered verses, and bells in the even-numbered verses.

43 Sweet Polly Oliver

traditional English

As sweet Polly Oliver lay musing in bed,
A sudden strange fancy came into her head;
'Nor father nor mother shall make me false prove!
I'll 'list for a soldier and follow my love.'

So early next morning she softly arose,
She dressed herself up in her dead brother's
 clothes;
She cut her hair close and she stained her face
 brown,
And went for a soldier to fair London town.

Then up spake the sergeant one day at his drill;
'Now who's good for nursing? A Captain lies ill.'
'I'm ready,' says Polly: to nurse him she's gone,
And finds 'tis her true love all wasted and wan.

The first week the doctor kept shaking his head:
'No nursing, young fellow, can save him,' he said.
But when Polly Oliver had nursed him back his life,
He cried, 'You have cherished him as if you were
 his wife!'

Oh then Polly Oliver she burst into tears,
And told the good doctor her hopes and her fears;
And very soon after, for better, for worse,
The Captain took joyfully his pretty soldier
 nurse.

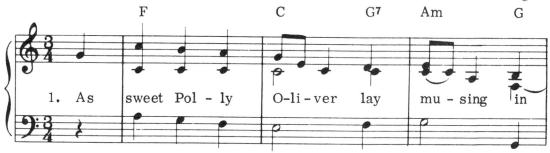

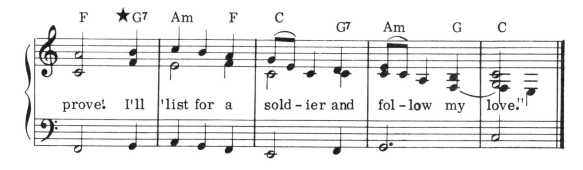

44 Blow away the morning dew

words: traditional Engli
melody: traditional Iri

1 My father bought at great expense
A grand high-stepping grey,
But when he put her at a fence
She backs and backs away.

And sing blow away the morning dew,
The rose and the rue,
Blow away the morning dew,
How sweet the winds do blow.

2 My mother bought a likely hen
On last St Martin's day;
She clucks and clucks and clucks again
But never yet will lay.
And sing blow away the morning dew ...

3 Oh Mustard is my brother's dog
Who whines and wags his tail,
And snuffs into the market bag
But dare not snatch the meal.
And sing blow away the morning dew ...

4 When walls lie down for steeds to step,
When eggs themselves go lay,
And the groats jump into Mustard's jaws,
To you my court I'll pay.
And sing blow away the morning dew ...

rue: a plant with a bitter taste used as a culinary herb. The leaves are
chopped finely and added to salads.
St. Martin's day: the 11 November. If the weather is fine around that date
it is known as St. Martin's summer.
groat: coarse oatmeal

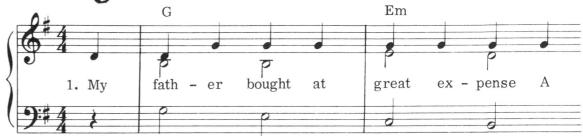

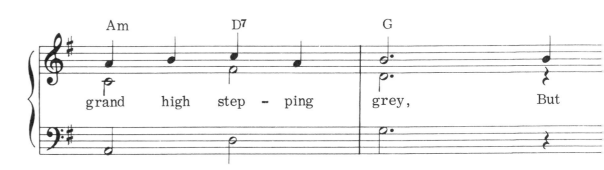

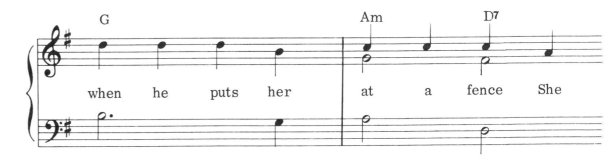

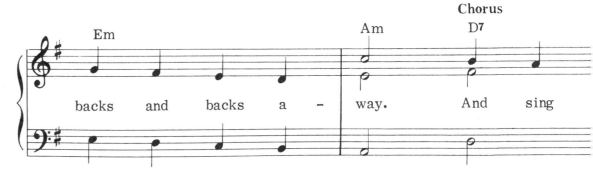

blow a-way the morn-ing dew, The
(G) (G) (G) (E) (E) (D) (D)

rose and the rue,

Blow a-way the morn-ing dew, How
(D') (B) (G) (A) (B) (G) (E)

sweet the winds do blow.

Play-along ideas

Verse
Tambours and tambourines
Maintain a steady beat throughout:

My fa - ther bought at great ex - pense ...

Chorus
Triangle
Play the rhythm of the words 'Blow away the morning dew' whenever they occur.

Xylophone
Play the melody for the words 'Blow away the morning dew' each time - the encircled letters below the music indicate which notes to play.

45 Suo-gân

traditional Welsh

1 Sleep, my baby, rest, my loved one,
   Softly slumber now with me,
   Clasped in mother's arms so tender,
   Warm in mother's love for thee.
   Naught shall ever come to harm thee
   While my loving watch I keep,
   Thou, my pretty one, shall slumber
   While I sing thy lullaby.

2 Sleep, my baby, rest, my loved one,
   While the evening shadows creep.
   Why, my dearest, art thou smiling,
   Smiling sweetly in thy sleep?
   Can it be that all the angels
   In God's Heaven smile on thee?
   Rest, my darling, smile and slumber
   While I sing thy lullaby.

Gân: means 'song' in Welsh, and suo-gân means 'lullaby'.

Play-along ideas

Glockenspiel or chime bars - D, E, F♯, G, A, B, C♯, D' (high D) and E' (high E)

The encircled letters below the music indicate which notes to play and when.

Triangle
Play gently on the first syllable of every line of the song.

46 O can ye sew cushions?

Scottish lullaby

1 O can ye sew cushions, and can ye sew sheets,
   And can you sing balaloo when my bonnie greets?
   And hee and baw birdie, and hee and baw lamb,
   And hee and baw birdie my bonnie wee lamb.

   Hee-o, haw-o, what'll I do with you?
   Black's the life that I lead with you.
   Many of you; little to give you,
   Hee-o, haw-o, what'll I do with you?

2 Now hush-a-by lammie, and hush-a-by dear,
   Now hush-a-by lammie, your mother is here.
   The wild wind is raving, your mother's heart's sore,
   The wild wind is raving, but you care no more.
      Hee-o, haw-o, what'll I do with you? …

3 Sing balaloo lammie, sing balaloo dear,
   Does wee lammie know that its daddy's not here?
   You're rocking quite sweetly on mother's warm knee,
   But daddy's a-rocking upon the salt sea.
      Hee-o, haw-o, what'll I do with you? …

greets: cries

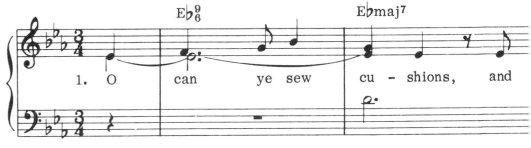

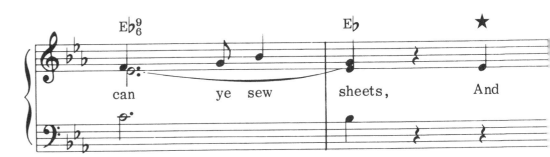

hee and baw bird – ie, and hee and baw lamb, And

hee and baw bird – ie my bon – nie wee lamb.

Chorus

Hee – o, haw – o, what'll I do with you? Black's the life that I lead with you.

Man – y of you; lit–tle to give you, Hee – o, haw – o, what'll I do with you?

Play-along ideas

Verse
Chime bar - B♭
Play on every strong beat:

O can ye sew cu - shions, and

Chorus   Guiro
Play the rhythm of the words
for the first four syllables of
each line of the chorus.

47 Barbara Allen

traditional (English son

1 In Reading town there I was born,
  In Scotland was my dwelling;
  I courted there a pretty maid,
  Her name was Barbara Allen.

2 I courted her for months and years,
  Thinking that I should gain her;
  And oft I vowed and did declare,
  No other man should have her.

3 I sent a man to yonder town,
  To ask for Barbara Allen;
  'You must come to my master's house,
  If you be Barbara Allen.'

4 So slowly she put on her clothes,
  So slowly she came to him;
  And when she came to his bedside,
  'Young man,' she said, 'You're dying.'

5 He turned his face unto the wall
  And death came slowly to him,
  'Adieu, adieu to all my friends,
  Farewell to Barbara Allen.'

6 And as she walked across the field
  And heard his death bell tolling,
  And every toll it seemed to say,
  'Hard hearted Barbara Allen.'

7 'Oh mother dear, make me my bed,
  And make it for my sorrow.
  A young man died for me today,
  I'll die for him tomorrow.'

Second tune

traditional (Scottish air)

1. In Read-ing town there I was born, In Scot-land was my

dwel-ling; I court-ed there a pret-ty maid, Her

name was Bar-bara Al-len. 2. I court-ed her for

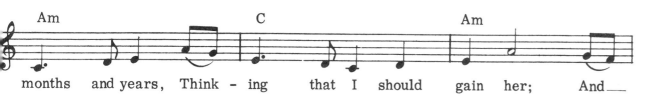

months and years, Think-ing that I should gain her; And

oft I vowed and did de-clare, No oth-er man should have her.

8 So he did die on one good day,
And she died on the morrow,
Oh, he did die for love of her,
And she did die for sorrow.

Historical notes

There are countless variations of this song, of which two are given here. Both the English and the Scottish claim the original song in different versions. The great diaryist Samuel Pepys knew this song. In his diary for 2 January 1666 he tells of the singing of 'Barbary Allen'.

Play-along ideas

First tune
Tuned percussion - C and G together
The encircled letters below the music indicate when to play.

Second tune
Tambour
Improvise in the style of the melody rhythm, tapping the skin with the fingers and alternating left and right hands.

48 Mush, mush

1 Oh, 'twas there I learned readin' an' writin',
At Billy Brackett's where I went to school,
An' 'twas there I learned 'owlin' an' fightin'
With me schoolmaster Mister O'Toole.
'Im an' me we 'ad many a scrimmage,
An' devil a copy I wrote,
There was ne'er a gossoon in the village
Dared tread on the tail o' me

    Mush, mush, mush tural-i-addy,
    Sing mush, mush, mush tural-i-ay.
    There was ne'er a gossoon in the village
    Dared tread on the tail o' me coat.

2 Oh 'twas there that I learned all me courtin',
Oh the lessons I took in the art,
Till Cupid, the blackguard, while sportin',
An arrow drove straight through my heart.
Judy O'Connor she lived just near me
An' tender lines to her I wrote.
If ye dare say one hard word against her
I'll tread on the tail o' your
    Mush, mush, mush tural-i-addy …

3 But a blackguard called Micky Maloney
Came an' stole her affections away
For he'd money, an' I hadn't any,
So I sent him a challenge next day.
In the evenin' we met at the Woodbine,
The Shannon we crossed in a boat,
An' I lathered 'im with me shillaly
For he trod on the tail o' me
    Mush, mush, mush tural-i-addy …

4   Oh me fame went abroad through the nation,
    An' folks came a-flockin' to see,
    An' they cried out without hesitation
    'You're a fightin' man Billy McGee.'
    Oh I've cleaned out the Finnigan faction
    An' I've licked all the Murphies afloat,
    If you're in for a fight or a ruction,
    Just tread on the tail o' me
          Mush, mush, mush tural-i-addy …

scrimmage: scuffle
gossoon: lad
blackguard: scoundrel
lathered him: gave him a beating
shillally: shillelagh (shill-ay-ly); an Irish cudgel of
blackthorn or oak

49 The tree in the wood

1 All in a wood there grew a tree,
  The finest tree you ever did see,
  And the green leaves grew around,
    around, around,
  And the green leaves grew around.

2 And on this tree there was a limb,
  The finest limb you ever did see,
  The limb was on the tree,
  The tree was in the wood,
  And the green leaves grew around,
    around, around,
  And the green leaves grew around.

3 And on this limb there was a branch,
  The finest branch you ever did see, (to 3 opposite)

4 And on this branch there was a nest,
  The finest nest you ever did see, (to 4)

5 And in this nest there was an egg,
  The finest egg you ever did see, (to 5)

6 And in this egg there was a yolk,
  The finest yolk you ever did see, (to 6)

7 And in this yolk there was a bird,
  The finest bird you ever did see, (to 7)

8 And on this bird there was a wing,
  The finest wing you ever did see, (to 8)

9 And on this wing there was a feather,
  The finest feather you ever did see, (to 9)

9 The feather was on the wing,
8 The wing was on the bird,
7 The bird was in the yolk,
6 The yolk was in the egg,
5 The egg was in the nest,
4 The nest was on the branch,
3 The branch was on the limb,
2 The limb was on the tree,
1 The tree was in the wood,
   And the green leaves grew around,
     around, around,
   And the green leaves grew around.

* this bar is repeated as necessary

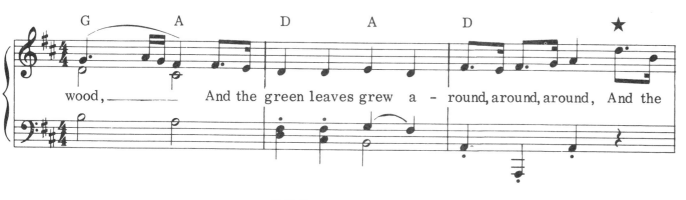

50 Widdicombe Fair

traditional English

1. Tom Pearce, Tom Pearce lend me your grey mare,
   All along, down along, out along lee.
   For I want for to go to Widdicombe Fair

   With Bill Brewer, Jan Stewer,
   Peter Gurney, Peter Davy,
   Dan'l Widdon, Harry Hawk,
   Old Uncle Tom Cobbleigh and all,
   Old Uncle Tom Cobbleigh and all.

2. And when shall I see again my grey mare?
   All along, down along, out along lee.
   By Friday soon, or Saturday noon,
   With Bill Brewer, Jan Stewer …

3. So they harnessed and bridled the old grey mare,
   All along, down along, out along lee.
   And off they drove to Widdicombe Fair,
   With Bill Brewer, Jan Stewer …

4. Then Friday came and Saturday noon,
   All along, down along, out along lee.
   But Tom Pearce's old mare have not trotted home,
   With Bill Brewer, Jan Stewer …

5. So Tom Pearce he got up to the top of the hill,
   All along, down along, out along lee.
   And he seed his old mare down a-making her will,
   With Bill Brewer, Jan Stewer …

6. So Tom Pearce's old mare her took sick and died,
   All along, down along, out along lee.
   And Tom he sat down on a stone and he cried,
   With Bill Brewer, Jan Stewer …

7 But this isn't the end of this shocking affair,
 All along, down along, out along lee.
 Nor, though they be dead, of the horrid career,
 With Bill Brewer, Jan Stewer …

8 When the wind whistles cold on the moor of a night,
 All along, down along, out along lee.
 Tom Pearce's old mare does appear ghastly white
 With Bill Brewer, Jan Stewer …

9 And all the night long be heard skirling and groans,
 All along, down along, out along lee.
 From Tom Pearce's old mare and a rattling of bones,
 With Bill Brewer, Jan Stewer …

skirling: shrill crying or shrieking
The spelling of this well known village on Dartmoor is now 'Widecombe'.

Play-along ideas

Wood block and tambourine
Lightly tap the rhythm of the words in the second line of the verse and the last line of the chorus.

Tuned percussion - D and E
The encircled letters below the music indicate when to play each note.

Bass drum
Play along with the tuned percussion. Then play after the very last word: 'all' as shown in the music.

51 Johnny Todd

1 Johnny Todd, he took a notion,
For to cross the ocean wide,
And he left his love behind him
Weeping by the Liverpool tide.

2 For a week she wept full sorely,
Tore her hair and wrung her hands,
Then she met another sailor
Walking on the Liverpool sands.

3 'Why fair maiden are you a-weeping
For your Johnny gone to sea?
If you'll wed with me tomorrow,
I will kind and constant be.

4 I will buy you sheets and blankets
I'll buy you a wedding ring,
You will have a silver cradle,
For to rock your babies in.'

5 Johnny Todd came home from sailing,
Sailing o'er the ocean wide
For to find his fair and false one
Was another sailor's bride.

6 All young men who go a-sailing,
For to fight the foreign foe,
Never leave your love, like Johnny,
Marry her before you go.

Acknowledgments

The publishers would like to thank Sue Wesselman and Vic Whitburn for their help in compiling this book.

Thanks are also due to Barrie Carson-Turner for researching the historical notes and to Rachel Taylor and Claire Weatherhead for their help in the preparation of this second edition.

Piano arrangements are by Sheena Hodge, Brian Hunt, Peter Nickol, Timothy Roberts and Sue Williams. Play along ideas are by Maureen Hanke, Sheena Hodge and Barrie Carson-Turner.

The following copyright owners have kindly granted their permission for the reprinting of words and music:

Chester Music Ltd for 8 'Billy Boy' from The Shanty Book collected and edited by Sir R R Terry. Reproduced by permission of G Schirmer Limited t/a J Curwen & Sons Limited. 8-9 Frith Street, London W1D 3JB

Novello & Company Ltd for 35 'Bushes and Briars' collected and arranged by Ralph Vaughan Williams. Reproduced by permission of Novello & Company Ltd. 8-9 Frith Street, London W1D 3JB.

Roberton Publications for 'Mairi's wedding' and 'Air fa-la-la-lo'. © 1938. Used by permission of Roberton Publications, a part of Goodmusic Publishing.

Stainer & Bell for 5 'Spinning wheel song' -The Virgin's Cradle Hymn (Lullaby of the Spinning Wheel). Music by F T Durrant. Words translated from the Latin by Samuel Taylor Coleridge. © 1936 Stainer & Bell Ltd.

Mrs Ursula Vaughan Williams for 25 'All things are quite silent'.

Every effort has been made to trace and acknowledge copyright owners. If any right has been omitted, the publishers offer their apologies and will rectify this in subsequent editions following notification.

Guitar chords

× string should not be sounded
° open string
⌒ 'barre' - two or more strings held down by one finger

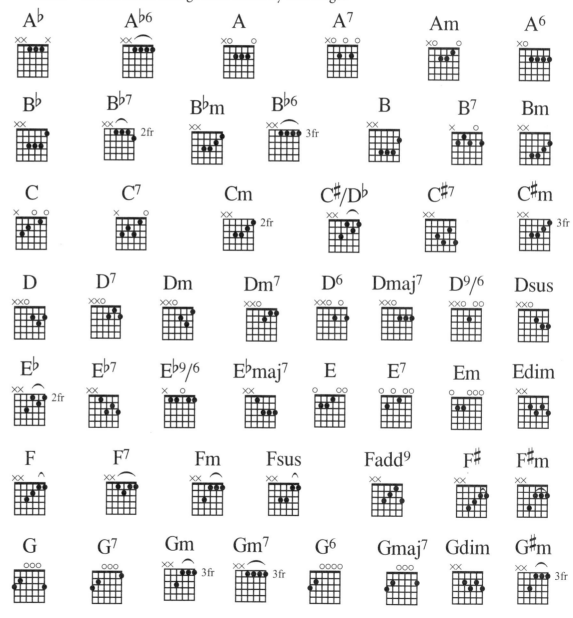

Index of first lines

Index of titles

More music books from A & C Black!

Agogo bells to xylophone
A commonsense guide to classroom percussion for the busy teacher. Clear descriptions and illustrations, origins and pronunciations, and diagrams and directions for playing - for over fifty common classroom percussion instruments.

The singing sack - new edition
A collection of stories and songs from around the world for 7-11 year olds. A multi-cultural resource for developing singing and literacy skills. Includes a CD of all the songs.

Nonsense songs
Michael Rosen's collection of silly songs for all ages, with acrobatic actions, rappy rhymes and very silly sounds. Excellent for developing singing and literacy skills. Includes a CD of the piano accompaniments.

Three rapping rats
Traditional and original stories with songs, raps and ways into composition for 7-9 year olds. No music reading required.

Ta-ra-ra boom-de-ay
A century of the best-loved songs from Victorian times to the Beatles in one songbook, with a separate singalong CD also available.

STRAWBERRY FAIR

A musical merry-go-round of 51 best-known, best-loved
traditional songs from around the British Isles. Includes:
Cockles and mussels, Skye boat song, Danny Boy, Suo-gân, Strawberry Fair,
Charlie is my darling, Green grow the rushes ho!

This beautiful new edition now includes a singalong CD of all
the piano accompaniments.

www.acblack.com **£14.99**
including VAT on CD

ISBN 0-7136-5832-0

9 780713 658323

90200

A & C Black • London